GALILEO

FIRST OBSERVER

OF MARVELOUS THINGS

BY THE SAME AUTHOR

ALBERT EINSTEIN

GALILEO

FIRST OBSERVER

OF MARVELOUS THINGS

BY

Elma Ehrlich Levinger

KINGSTON HOUSE · CHICAGO

PUBLISHED ORIGINALLY BY JULIAN MESSNER, INC.

NEW YORK

PUBLISHED SIMULTANEOUSLY IN CANADA

BY THE COPP CLARK COMPANY LTD.

DEDICATED MOST GRATEFULLY

to

DR. VINCENT S. MEYER

TABLE OF CONTENTS

GALILEO

FIRST OBSERVER

OF MARVELOUS THINGS

"I give infinite thanks to God who has been pleased to make me the First Observer of Marvelous Things."

—FROM A LETTER WRITTEN BY GALILEO
VENICE, JANUARY 30, 1610

FOREWORD

Writing the story of Galileo has been a delightful but often a difficult task. Many of the best authorities on Galileo's life differ on matters both trivial and important. Did he have two or three sisters? Just what was the social status of Marina Gamba? What changes did Galileo promise the Holy Office he would make in his masterwork, which was to bring him disgrace and suffering? In every case I have tried to select the facts which have seemed to me most reasonable.

The letters of Galileo, his daughter and fellow scientists are unchanged, except when it was necessary to cut for space. It also seemed necessary to cut down the accounts of both Galileo's trial and his recantation. I have given what I consider the essential portions of these two important documents; but I have cut them down drastically, as legal proceedings seldom interest the reader.

Obviously much of the dialogue is my own invention; but in every case I tried to have the scientist and his family and his friends speak "according to character." And, I must confess, I deviated from history by dovetailing or entirely omitting a number of well-established facts. Again, a matter of length! Galileo lived a very long and a very rich life. Had I told all, this biography could easily have stretched into a second volume.

ELMA EHRLICH LEVINGER

Los Altos, California,
    May, 1952

A LAMP SWINGS IN THE
CATHEDRAL

HE HAD ENTERED the cathedral to pray, but he was not praying. Although his long, nervous fingers told the beads of
his rosary, for once the accustomed action brought no peace to
the troubled university student. For weeks Galileo Galilei had
been disturbed and unhappy. Now, while his fingers and lips
moved in seeming harmony, his restless brain sent hammers
beating behind his temples. Although nothing of importance
had happened, Galileo suddenly felt he could no longer endure
the annoyances and doubts which were making his life at the
University of Pisa unbearable.

The twenty-year-old student forced himself to face his
troubles with the same cool detachment he had always given
to his forbidden mathematical studies. What is wrong with me?
he asked himself. Who is to blame that I am facing failure and
may be expelled from the university? And if I finally manage to
graduate, he thought bitterly, it will be as I have warned my
father a hundred times: I will never become a rich and successful doctor.

1

Ever since the birth of his oldest son in Pisa in 1564, Vincenzio Galilei had looked forward to the day when he might close his despised shop, leaving his first-born—Galileo—to support the family. From earliest childhood Galileo had realized that his father's life had never been an easy one. Born of a noble family which had given a number of distinguished officials, artists and soldiers to the state of Tuscany, but now knew only abasement and poverty, Vincenzio Galilei had been forced to put aside the dreams of his early manhood. A skilled musician, the author of several books on musical subjects, he soon discovered how difficult it was to support his demanding wife Giulia and the children she bore him. In spite of his lineage, he felt no shame in turning to trade, now that the Medici bankers and the merchant princes of the Venetian republic ruled their city-states.

But Vincenzio shrank from spending the rest of his life haggling over the counters of the little wool shop which he opened in Florence shortly after Galileo's birth. How could the boy know that his father's ever-increasing irritability, his impatience with his sons were due to his fear of the future? For the elder Galilei was haunted by his dread of poverty. He saw himself and his family driven from the small but decent stone house that sheltered them to a miserable wooden shanty or airless, damp cellar. Whenever he passed one of the miserable beggars who infested the city's streets, he shuddered to think of himself and his children depending on charity for the miserable crusts which kept them alive.

Somehow the disappointed musician dared to hope that his oldest son would eventually redeem the family fortune. Had the child not been named after one of the most famous of his ancestors, Galileo Galilei, the physician, still renowned in Florence? And did ever a boy give such early promise of a dazzling career? Vincenzio would often ask his wife, only to be answered with a skeptical shrug.

How well Galileo remembered those household scenes in the lovely Tuscan city from which he had come to near-by Pisa to enroll in the university! Brooding now in the dim, quiet cathedral, the stocky redheaded student recalled his father's touching pride and early hopes.

"Consider his musical talent!" Vincenzio would exclaim. He delighted in teaching the little fellow to play the organ and the flute. "Someday," he encouraged, "you will be the most favored musician in the court of the Grand Duke of Tuscany. Not a poor merchant like your father who now plays only for his own pleasure."

"Will music bring any more bread to his mouth than it did to yours?" Galileo remembered his mother grumbling.

But young Galileo himself had dreamed of becoming a painter. His early pictures won praise even in Florence which overflowed with treasures from the Renaissance. Jacopo da Empoli actually brought his pictures to Galileo for criticism; the great artist declared that the youth's knowledge of perspective had guided him in all his work.

"If our son might only devote his life to art!" dreamed Vincenzio one night as he rolled up the last bolt of cloth and locked the door of his shop. "It may be a fortunate omen that he first saw the light not far from the birthplace of Leonardo da Vinci. And you remember, Giulia, that our Galileo was born in the very month that Michelangelo died."

His wife, counting the few coins in the iron box beneath the counter, laughed scornfully.

"You are right," agreed Vincenzio, answering her unspoken

protest. "Unless he become a Michelangelo or a Raphael or a Cellini, he may have to struggle as I have all my life to make a living."

Galileo could still see himself curled up on a settle in a corner of the shop. He could still smell through the open door the odor of the streets, which needed a heavy rain to wash the accumulated garbage down into the Arno. The boy had felt a twinge of remorse as he caught the note of weariness in his father's gentle voice and noticed the discouraged droop of his shoulders beneath the shabby coat. But soon Galileo fell to dreaming of selling one of the inventions at which he loved to tinker from morning until night, of coming with a bag of florins to empty into his mother's lap. Maybe then she would hold her complaining tongue, while he told her to buy a new dress for herself and shoes for his sisters—yes, and sugar plums for her favorite toddling son.

From his earliest years Galileo had tried to devise toys for himself, fascinating with wheels and pulleys, toys so attractive that his sisters and brother often snatched them away, and even his father admired their ingenuity.

"You should have lived a hundred years ago, my son," Vincenzio told him. "For you are truly a child of the Renaissance. In those golden days a man might be a musician and poet and artist—and workman. He might compose the melodies he played and cast his own statues like Benvenuto Cellini. Or like Leonardo da Vinci mix his own paints, though not always successfully. Just the other day a traveler who saw his 'Last Supper' in Milan told me that due to the dampness of the convent walls, the colors are already fading. Yes, God gave Leonardo more of His gifts than any man has ever received from His hand before, or is ever like to receive again. For he knew mechanics as well as anatomy and art, and the engines of war which he invented—"

"When I am grown up, I shall invent greater things," the boy interrupted.

"I should box your ears for your unseemly boasting," Vincenzio chided. But a moment later he smiled indulgently and patted the rough, auburn head. "You have very clever fingers, my son. But do not permit your skill to make you vainglorious like Da Vinci. True, he achieved both wealth and honor. But he had the pride of Lucifer and like Lucifer he was punished for his pride. Was it not for his many sins that he died far from our beautiful Florence, a sad end to all his glory, although the King of France smoothed his dying pillow!"

Vincenzio shook his head sadly over a doom any true son of Florence might lament. Next to his family, the wool merchant loved the proud city that ruled the Tuscan state, a city as mighty as its rival Venice, a city fairer than Rome itself.

"Pride and impious curiosity helped to bring Leonardo low," he continued. "Not that it is wrong to ask questions as you are always doing," he amended hastily. "When I was very young I, too, always had a question on my tongue; sometimes I actually doubted the wisdom of my elders. In my book on counterpoint, I wrote . . . . But one learns as he grows older to be satisfied with the truths that have come down to us through the ages."

Galileo had only half listened.

"Father," he said suddenly, "I think when I grow up I shall be an inventor like Leonardo da Vinci."

"Then learn to curb your ambition which Leonardo could never do. Did I ever tell you that after studying the flight of birds, he dared to try to construct a flying machine? It was only by the grace of God that he was not dashed to pieces when the poor, flimsy thing collapsed. Like Icarus who strove to reach the sun! How could such a great genius imagine that men could ever fly!"

"Perhaps," boasted Galileo, "when I am a grown man, I shall build a machine that will fly."

This time Vincenzio, who for all his indulgent pride knew when a child should be put in his place, boxed his son's ears.

What could one do with such a boy? He needed the discipline of books and of wise teachers who would win his respect for their learning. Why not send the too-cocky stripling to the monastery school at Vallombrosa? There, decided Vincenzio, the Benedictine monks, steeped in the knowledge of Aristotle and St. Thomas Aquinas, would cure his giddy ideas and prepare him to study for a lucrative profession.

The plan succeeded only too well. Because of his quick mind and retentive memory Galileo soon became a favorite pupil. For a while his active hands no longer itched to create. His eager brain no longer questioned, but was content to absorb all the wisdom of the huge books the kindly fathers set before him. "How lucky I am to live after printing has been invented!" Galileo rejoiced. "In the olden days when everything the ancients taught had to be written down on scrolls, only a few people could read and study them. I shall try to read all the great books that have ever been written. Then I shall know the truth about everything."

He became so charmed with the scholar's life that he decided to become a monk. He wanted nothing better than to spend the rest of his life in the quiet, peaceful library at Vallombrosa, or to walk under the pines and chestnuts which filled the air with their pungent sweetness and seemed to stand like sentinels to shut out a troublesome world.

Vincenzio Galilei, although a devout son of the Church, had more ambitious plans for his gifted boy. True, a youth with Galileo's intellect might hope to rise rapidly to a high position; he might in time restore the glory of the family name by becoming a bishop, even a cardinal! But Vincenzio shrewdly realized that although his son had grown disciplined and quiet under monastic tutelage, he might at any time be seized by one of his mad whims.

Suppose, worried the father, Galileo should begin to long for the silly inventions with which he used to tinker? Or question the wisdom he now drank in so eagerly? And, with his unpolished manners and stubbornness, would he ever learn to be enough of a politician to rise in the ranks of the hierarchy? Would he not be more likely to estrange the very superiors who were able to secure his promotion? Perhaps he would be content to remain a humble scholar monk all his life, studying and teaching.

Then what would become of the father's dreams of a serene old age? Who would provide dowries for the daughters? Who would pay for the long training for Michelagnolo, who was already showing promise of excelling Vincenzio as a musician?

"My son, I will not permit you to become a monk. Tomorrow you will return with me to Florence," decreed Vincenzio.

Now as he mused in the cathedral, grown dim with the evening shadows, Galileo smiled grimly as he remembered his protesting question and his father's answer.

"But, Father, if I do not become a monk and devote my life to study, what else is there for me to do?"

"I have thought long and seriously of your future," Vincenzio assured him. "You have often heard me speak of our famous ancestor Galileo Galilei. Have you ever thought why I gave you his illustrious name? I am sure," he went on solemnly, for like the majority of his contemporaries he was a firm believer in astrology, "that I divined somehow it was written in your horoscope that you, too, should become a great physician. Study medicine and you will become rich and famous."

Somehow Vincenzio managed to gather together sufficient funds to support the boy as a medical student at the University of Pisa. From the first Galileo hated the very thought of studying medicine. Perhaps his dislike was rooted in a senseless obstinacy against his father's authority. And since the youth was blessed with a scientific mind, he hated from the first the methods and superstitions of even the leading physicians of his day.

What was the use, he asked himself angrily, of listening to lectures based on the ancient authorities Hippocrates and Galen, when a student was never encouraged to experiment and perhaps to discover new truths for himself? The lessons in anatomy meant so little; a professor read a description of the organs to be studied; another teacher explained the passage at great length. Finally, assisted by several senior students, the lecturer would illustrate his remarks with a dissection of the body before him. Galileo tried to listen attentively; but his fingers worked impatiently below the long sleeves of his scholar's gown. Why, oh why, was he not permitted to wield the scalpel himself!

He became disgusted with the medical profession when he realized that respected physicians still prescribed pulverized unicorn horn for a poisoned patient. He could not respect a teacher who seriously explained that because the various parts of the body corresponded to certain signs of the zodiac, herbs to cure diseases of these organs must be gathered during the ascent of corresponding symbols. His only consolation was that his medical courses included the philosophical studies he loved at Vallombrosa.

Galileo was also interested in mathematics. He begged his father to allow him to drop his classes in medicine that he might devote all of his time to this fascinating subject.

Vincenzio was outraged.

"Why did God give me a fool for a son?" he demanded. "Instead of forcing you to help me in the shop, I give you the opportunity I never enjoyed of preparing for an honored profession. Which you would forsake for mathematics! Mathematics, bah! The science is held in such little respect that there is not a single professor to teach the subject at your university. I have heard," he ended, darkly, "that you actually stand listening in the corridor while the young duke receives instruction from Ostilio Ricci, the court mathematician. Tomorrow I shall speak to the royal tutor and see that you are driven out of the palace the next time you run away from your classes to listen to his nonsense."

Vincenzio had made good his threat and now Galileo was forced to learn what he could of his favorite subject without instruction. More and more he neglected his medical studies; more and more he annoyed his professors by demanding a reason for every fact they stated in the classroom.

"But, Master, how can you prove what you just said?" the young rebel would demand.

"It must be true because it stands written in our books," came the answer, usually followed by a citation from the accepted authority, the Greek philosopher Aristotle.

Only that morning the youth had dared to challenge one of his teachers with the statement: "You say what you tell us must be true because it is found in the works of Aristotle. But suppose Aristotle made a mistake!"

The gray-haired professor and most of the class had shuddered at such blasphemy. It was as though Galileo had denied the existence of God, or dared to defend the little-known theory of Copernicus—that the earth actually moved around the sun.

For a moment the teacher sputtered in helpless anger. At last he found his voice and spoke coldly. "Until you learn to curb your unruly tongue and behave with proper respect, young man, I will not permit you to enter this lecture hall."

Blushing with anger and shame, Galileo hastily left the room; he tried not to hear the jibes of many of his classmates who seemed pleased with his disgrace. "Why do they hate me so?" he asked himself, as he mused with bowed head in the dusty cathedral. "Am I a criminal because I want to find the truth?"

From behind a column at the far end of the cathedral a dark-robed verger came bearing a long, slender torch. In the distance the flame seemed a bright star, now glowing, now momentarily extinguished when thrust into the bowl of one of the swinging lamps. One by one they glowed through the gathering darkness. At last the verger paused near the corner where Galileo slouched against a column. The rosary still dangled from his fingers; his youthful face was furrowed with his unhappy musings.

Suddenly Galileo started forward. His face was no longer haggard with bitterness, but keen with interest and curiosity; his eyes, sparkling with excitement, stared at the nearest lamp. When lighting it, the verger had started it swaying on the long iron chains which fastened it to the ceiling.

Passing to where the shadows were blackest, the verger, unaware of leaving a revelation behind him, lit another lamp and left it swaying upon the long iron chains.

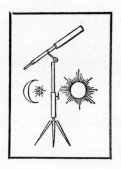

DOUBTFUL TRIUMPH

THE VERGER, MOVING slowly with his torch through the dimness, never dreamed that the swinging lamp was as meaningful in the progress of science as the first glimpse of a new continent's green shores to an Italian explorer a hundred years before. Nor could the youthful Galileo himself realize that at the end of his stormy life he would turn back to his first great discovery and plan a new use for the pendulum. Now only one thought possessed him. Triumphantly he repeated again and again: "Aristotle was wrong! Now I can prove that he was wrong!"

Even as his eyes flamed with defiance, the twenty-year-old student realized that to battle against Aristotle openly would call for almost as much courage as the German monk Luther had displayed in his attacks on the Catholic church.

For Aristotle, greatest of the Greek philosophers, for two thousand years had ruled over the minds of scholars—Moslem, Jewish and Christian. The learned, from the greatest to the least, acknowledged his authority in every field of human knowledge. Thomas Aquinas, the sainted Dominican friar, in the later half of the thirteenth century had reconciled the pagan teacher's views of the universe with the teachings of Holy Scripture. Only here and there a rebel had dared to hint that the master's works contained an occasional error.

Among his many books on many subjects Aristotle had written a work on physics. Reading and rereading this authoritative work, Galileo had puzzled over Aristotle's statement that falling bodies reach the earth at varying speeds, depending on their weight. Said Aristotle—and no one had challenged him, at least publicly—that a heavier body would fall faster, a lighter body more slowly. But now to Galileo's own eyes the swinging cathedral lamp demonstrated that the infallible Greek had erred.

Centuries ago Aristotle had employed common-sense observation. The son of a physician, he was greatly interested in plants and animals and made a noteworthy collection of those found in his own country and Asia Minor. His pupil Alexander the Great, in his long journeys to conquer new worlds paused in his travels to send back to his old tutor specimens from lands as far off as India.

The facts that Aristotle collected so untiringly and set down in his works were seldom questioned during the Middle Ages, when his fame was so firmly established that it was sufficient to refer to him merely as The Philosopher. And few scholars added to the Greek's store of learning. There were noteworthy exceptions such as Albert the Great, the Dominican friar, who taught at the University of Paris in the thirteenth century; and his contemporary, the Franciscan Roger Bacon, professor at Oxford, renowned for his work in optics. But it is noteworthy that their methods seemed so sensational in their own day that both of these worthies actually figured in legends as magicians.

Now it happened that Galileo, although he stated publicly that he greatly admired Aristotle's writings on drama and politics, dared in spite of his youth to challenge the philosopher's scientific teaching. He had always longed to prove every new fact before accepting and applying it. And this humble student did a strange thing for that age when it was the accepted thing to base every argument solely on faith in authority. He resolved to prove what he believed the truth, to repeat for himself the demonstration of the swinging lamp!

At that moment the controlled experiment of the laboratory, as we know it today, was born.

Hurrying back to his mean garret room, he bolted the door against his noisy fellow students. All that night he sat on his bed, pondering on what he had seen. Early the next morning he hurried from shop to shop to find where he could buy cheapest what he needed for his experiment. Two iron chains; one was rusty, but it would serve his purpose. The chains cost only a few pennies, but even this outlay he could ill afford from the small allowance his father managed to send him. In another shop down the street the good-natured ironmonger told the excited youth to take what he needed from a huge pile of discarded pieces near the door. An iron ball, not large but very heavy, rewarded his search. Another of about half the weight would do.

There was no thought of morning lectures as Galileo again bolted his door. To one chain he fastened the larger ball, to the other the smaller. How could he attach them to reproduce the lamps which swung in the cathedral? The rough rafters above his head gave the answer. Back to the ironmonger who again allowed him to turn over the bits of junk in the pile beside the door. This time Galileo discovered two hooks, rust eaten and bent, which the ironmonger, greatly puzzled, obligingly pounded into shape with his great hammer.

Muttering hasty but fervent thanks, the student almost ran back to his lodgings. It took only a few minutes to screw the hooks into a rafter, to swing from them the two chains with their unequal weights.

Galileo swung the two chains into simultaneous motion. Breathless with anticipation, he watched them swing, now left, now right. Again and again they swung, the motion dying down slowly, until both chains hung motionless—at approximately the same instant.

No, Galileo thought, one trial is not enough. This may be an accident.

Again he swung the two chains; again they ceased to move after the same interval of motion. Again and yet again; always the same result.

Galileo sank upon his bed and wiped his sweaty brow with a trembling hand. Then he tried to control his excitement. He climbed on the room's one chair, leaned over the back and addressed an imaginary audience with the dignity and assurance of a professor lecturing to his students.

"Aristotle has made many errors," he began, "and I will now refute one of them from his theory of mechanics. He has stated —and our teachers have repeated his mistake—that when two bodies fall to the earth, the heavier body takes less time to reach the ground. These two bodies of unequal weight cannot fall because I have fastened them securely to the chains, just as the cathedral lamp was fastened. But when any one of them is set in motion, being flung through the air, it strives to fall. If Aristotle were correct, the heavier object would be the first to reassume its immobility. But, gentlemen, behold: I set the heavier and the lighter ball moving at the same time and at the same time they returned to their original positions."

At that moment he was too dazed with triumph to realize how easy it would be to make the same demonstration with freely falling bodies dropped from a height. Nor did he dream how the swaying, weighted chain could be transformed into an instrument to measure time. He was aware only of a growing giddiness, which made him glad to lie down upon his bed until he could calm himself.

In his temples he felt a pounding, pounding. It is as though that ironmonger—may God bless him for his kindness—were swinging his heavy hammer inside my skull, mused Galileo. Have my sleepless night, my fasting and all this excitement thrown me into a fever?

Galileo sat up and placed the fingers of his right hand, which still trembled, on his left wrist, as he had been taught to do in one of his medical classes. He remembered what he had once read in an essay of Leonardo da Vinci's, who had studied anatomy and physiology to help perfect himself in his drawing.

Yes, he mused, Leonardo was truly a poet. He had compared the flow of blood with the circulation of water from the hills to the rivers and the sea—from the sea to the clouds and back to the hills as rain. Now my blood surges like a mountain stream in the springtime. Yet, considered Galileo, in all my excitement there is a steady beat, a beat like the pounding in my head, like—like the even sway of those chains fastened from the ceiling.

Again he set the brass chains in motion. But now he no longer thought of confronting the partisans of the mistaken Aristotle. Intoxicated by a new idea, he wondered how he might time the flow of blood which throbbed beneath his wrists.

Again Galileo neglected his classes to play the scavenger at the junk pile. His new friend, the ironmonger, although an ignorant man was impressed when the student explained his invention.

Invited to share the good man's dinner of black bread and soup and sour red wine, Galileo pushed aside his scarcely tasted meal. Although cursed with a too-hearty appetite which his pittance from home was never able to satisfy, he was now too excited to eat.

"Now one must time the pulse beat by guesswork," said Galileo. "It would be different if every physician had a watch."

"I have heard that the King of France has one set in diamonds," murmured the ironmonger.

"Yes, yes"—impatiently—"and there is talk that some German prince, lately come to Rome, has presented one to the Holy Father. But since even our wealthiest doctors cannot hope to rival kings and popes, they will welcome the little instrument I shall make for them. See, I will draw it for you." Dipping his finger in the wine, he traced an outline on the bare wooden table top. "It is really nothing more than a little pendulum, a small weight fastened to a cord. But it will serve its purpose for it will accurately measure the pulse beat."

"Yes, every physician will use it," predicted Galileo's host. "You will sell it and grow rich. And then," he grinned, "after you buy yourself a pair of shoes to hide your toes, which now are creeping out so shamelessly to see the world, you will pay me for all my iron and brass. You will become a great physician, for never have I seen such a wise head on such young shoulders. And when I am ill you will attend me without a fee and use this curious toy I was privileged to see born."

The physicians of Pisa actually treated Galileo's invention with respect and many of them soon began to use his pulsifier for counting the pulses of their patients. But Galileo never be-

came a full-fledged doctor and had no opportunity of proving
the worth of his own instrument.

For he was too poor to continue his medical studies. He did
not receive a penny for his invention. His father, disgusted with
reports of the boy's lack of interest in his work, and really
unable to continue his allowance, refused to support him any
longer. Galileo was glad that he need no longer study for the
profession he bitterly despised. He had grown more and more
restless and unhappy at the university, where his attempted
refutation of Aristotle had met jeers when it did not bring
actual enmity. But what was there for him to do with his life
in Florence?

He tried to study in the shop, propping his beloved Euclid
against a bale of coarse woolen cloth or gleaming damask;
sometimes he tinkered with one of his inventions, which his
father disdained as "toys," unworthy of a man who had studied
at a great university. Or, excitedly clutching his quill until it
broke, Galileo would add a sentence to his essay on "Hydro-
statics, the Little Balance." But in the middle of a calculation, or
while he hunted for just the right word, his mother's shrill voice
ripped through the silence of his concentration.

"If you have nothing better to do than draw silly lines and
circles, help your overworked sisters and fetch water from the
well," she commanded.

Back at his studies, Galileo would force himself to listen
courteously to his father, just returned from a meeting of the
wool merchants' guild.

"True, we are not artists or musicians or scholars, but ours
is an honorable profession, which you may someday join without shame or regret. Help me in the shop that you may master
my trade and carry on the business when I am dead," decreed
the aging and sickly Vincenzio. "God forgive me for holding

you up as an example to your brother Michelagnolo. He has just enough brains to play the lute, but someday he may earn his own living with his music. But you, with all your talents, are a worthless idler; a full-grown man, you expect your old father to support you."

Through the Middle Ages European scholars had either been priests or members of religious orders or students supported by the Church. Now in the sixteenth century there were scholars who, like an author or artist or musician, depended on wealthy patrons. Stung into resentful action by his father's reproaches, Galileo tramped from palace to palace in Florence, armed with recommendations from the court mathematician Ostilio Ricci and several other learned men who believed in him and his future. Surely some prince or duke who loved learning might be impressed by the letters Galileo pleaded to place before him and would lend a helping hand. Or some nobleman, when reminded of the services rendered the state by several of Galileo's ancestors, would use his influence in the unhappy youth's behalf.

He learned to flatter the watchful lackeys that he might slip inside the tall iron gates they guarded. Then he would plead with a minor court official for a short audience—"only a minute, a little minute, sir!"—with the lord of the manor. Sometimes he managed to cajole his way into the presence of the great man himself.

If the prospective patron proved gracious, Galileo would try to demonstrate the worth of his inventions. Stammering with enthusiasm, he would explain the merits of his pulsifier; or he would exhibit his water scales. "Both practical, Your Grace, but neither has brought me a single penny for my pains! I am sure the esteemed Ostilio Ricci, your own court mathematician, has already told Your Highness—But if Your Grace will only observe for yourself—My hydrostatic balance, which is based on the principles of the Greek mathematician Archimedes—Surely, Your Grace recalls how when the king suspected baser metals in the gold of his crown—!"

At this point the noble listener, his mind occupied with the details of that morning's hunt or tonight's masque, might lean back in his great chair, nod assent and close his eyes for better concentration.

But Galileo would doggedly continue.

"I will not bore Your Grace with the details concerning the relative weight of the water which the immersed object displaces. Yet if you will grant me time to demonstrate the means by which this invention of mine measures the proportions of metals in an alloy—"

But in the middle of the inventor's hurried explanations, the lordling might smother a yawn and declare he had no time to listen to the plea of a new suitor. Or he would call his secretary to bring him some state documents or to take down an important letter.

Once a courtier was so impressed that he suggested the brilliant youth should be rewarded by an invitation to that evening's feasting.

Galileo borrowed from one of his cousins a presentable velvet cloak and a new plumed hat. Returning to the great man's villa perched on one of the hills overlooking Florence, the youth dreamed that through some miracle he might sit beside his noble host and tell him further of his invention. But the place of honor was occupied by Giovanni de Medici, bastard brother of the Grank Duke of Tuscany. Like so many gentlemen of his circle, the prince loved to dabble in mechanics. Tonight he babbled incessantly of his almost completed invention —a machine, boasted the amateur scientist, which would cer-

tainly prove invaluable in dredging the silt-filled harbor of Leg-
horn.

No one would listen to him if he sat in my place, thought
Galileo bitterly. It is harder to get a hearing if you sit below
the salt!

For a moment his eyes softened as they rested on the beauty
of the huge silver and gilt server which stood in its prescribed
place on the gleaming cloth. A nymph, her scanty metal
draperies so cleverly devised that they seemed to quiver in her
flight, poised on the rim. Galileo forgot his agitation as he
wondered what genius had devised the piece and decided it
almost equaled in loveliness the masterpiece Bevenuto Cellini had created for the French king a century before. But
he grew angry again; why should an ignoramus sit above the
salt, even though his father had been ruler of Tuscany? While
he, Galileo, whose achievements in his early twenties should
have brought him recognition, remained forgotten at the very
end of the long table, among the giggling ladies in waiting and
the effeminate pages?

Galileo was proud with more than his father's pride of an-
cestry. The complacency of the nobly born was now equaled
by the pride of the scholars who dreamed of ruling a new world
which they themselves hoped to create. Young as he was, the
unhappy university student felt he belonged to this new aris-
tocracy of learning. He keenly felt the injustice of being ignored
by the flunkeys who shared his lowly surroundings.

Only a very young page seemed about to greet him. But after
a scornful inventory of Galileo's borrowed velvet and plumes,
suddenly grown shabby in the richly appointed dining hall, the
boy turned his back on the unwelcome guest and began to ex-
change silly nothings with the lady in waiting across the table.

Galileo had already anticipated enjoying the rich and rare

foods which should have been a memorable treat after the sparse meals his mother served the family. Now for the macaroni and simply prepared greens usually set before him, he might gorge himself on elaborate salads and breast of partridge. He had long ago grown weary of Giulia's favorite dish of eggs served with vinegar sauce; but he knew better than to complain when his mother insisted that she could not afford to serve meat except on a feast day. Tonight he might dine on roast lamb, savory with spices. But Galileo found himself choking on every course, even the tempting, plump purple grapes heaped high on a silver platter.

As soon as the great ones at the head of the table rose to enjoy cards and music, Galileo wrapped his cloak around him and hurried down the wide marble stairs.

For a moment he paused to look down on the moon-whitened city below—his beloved Florence, home of his ancestors who had known wealth and honor within its many-towered walls. He could see the dim outlines of the Church of Santa Croce where many of his forefathers slept their last sleep among a goodly company: Machiavelli, Prince of Diplomats rested there, and Michelangelo, buried close to the pulpit with ceremonies and tributes a king might have envied.

Yet Michelangelo had also known bitterness and defeat. In his long life—at that moment Galileo prayed to be spared the emptiness and bitterness of old age—the Florentine sculptor had journeyed not only to the stars but the lowest depths of the pit. In Rome he had wrought the "Moses" which men declared surpassed the works of the Greeks; the glories of "Creation" and the griefs of the "Last Judgment." While this Church of Santa Croce was the pride of every citizen of Tuscany because her son had given it the statue of the Virgin sorrowing over the crucified Christ. Yet even Michelangelo Buonarroti, before

whom mighty rulers should have stood humbly, had known the
bitterness of seeking patronage of prince and pope.

Galileo paused again on the corner of that narrow street
where men still pointed out the stone on which, three hundred
years before, Dante had sat and pondered before he went into
exile. From a near-by tavern came the sound of drunken laughter and a rollicking song. Resting where Dante had rested,
Galileo wondered whether his own life would be as wretched.

As a child of Florence, Galileo had always considered the
singer of heaven and hell the greatest of all poets. He had
studied his writings so thoroughly that he had actually been
able to plot the topography of Dante's "Inferno." With his
marvelous memory, Galileo found it easy to recite passage after
passage of the *Divine Comedy*. Now, sitting in the soft moonlight, broken with discouragement, comparing his own evening's shame with Dante's humiliation in the halls of his
patrons, he began to recite in the musical Tuscan accent he
shared with the singer:

> "Yea, thou shalt learn how salt his food who fares
> Upon another's bread—how steep his path
> Who treadeth up and down another's stairs."

Tomorrow, thought Galileo despairingly, it would all begin
again. He would taste the bitterness of the bread his father
could ill afford to share with him and which his mother begrudged her idling son. He would climb the steep stairs of still
another palace, only to be greeted with contempt. Dropping his
head on his knees, Galileo sat weeping in the moonlight.

After a few days of brooding over his latest disappointment,
Galileo announced that he intended to set out to seek his fortune.

"Since I have failed to impress the great ones of Florence," he told his parents, "I will travel all over Italy; I will linger in every city where learned men gather, demonstrate to them how far I have progressed in my studies and, with God's approval, persuade them to recommend me to some patron."

"Where will you go?" asked Vincenzio, a gleam of interest brightening his tired eyes. He recalled how when a youth he also had dreamed of visiting strange, far-off places; but he had never journeyed beyond the borders of his native Tuscany.

Galileo had not yet mapped out his travels, but now he replied airily:

"I shall visit all the great Italian universities—Bologna, Padua—and, of course, I shall go to Rome. I have already read some of the works of the famed Jesuit scholar Christoforo Clavius, who teaches mathematics in the Roman College; I long to talk with him."

"And I suppose His Holiness will invite you to visit him," sneered Giulia. "It's a pity we can't afford to buy you a new doublet and cloak to impress him. And how will you live on the roads?"

"As poor students always do," answered Galileo lightly. "Lodging? A tired man rests as easily on straw in an outhouse as on a bed of down. Drink? Water from a wayside brook. Bread?" He laughed. "At Pisa I heard the story of a student who begged his way from the Netherlands to Paris, where he hoped to attend the university. He received nothing but crusts, some of them too hard to chew. So to keep up his spirits he composed a long Latin dissertation on the different degrees of staleness in the bread offered him, and recited it as he tramped along the highways."

Giulia was not amused. "You'll be glad to eat moldy crusts before you return to sit at a Christian table," she said. "At least

I'll give you a bundle of bread and cheese to keep your stomach from growling for the first few days of your journey."

A few months later Galileo returned home, footsore and as hungry as his mother had prophesied, tanned from the wind and sun, his body hardened, his mind enriched through his experiences. He brought back his most precious memories from Rome, which he visited for the first time in 1587.

Here he had been privileged to talk with Father Clavius, who had shown a genuine interest in the young scientist's writings and inventions. The Jesuit professor had recently been honored by a commission from the Pope to reform the calendar; praise from such an outstanding scholar meant much to the long-discouraged Galileo.

But when he returned to Florence, still doubtful of his future, Galileo learned that the court mathematician, Ricci, had good news for him. Not only Ostilio Ricci but several other prominent Florentines had been impressed by Galileo's scientific essays and his hydrostatic scales. There was no chair of mathematics at the University of Pisa, but these gentlemen persuaded the Grand Duke of Tuscany to create one and to appoint Galileo Galilei to fill the position.

"You will be among the most poorly paid of all the professors," mourned Vincenzio when he learned how little his son would receive yearly for teaching the neglected subject.

"Then how will you repay us for all the money we have spent to keep you in school?" As always his mother's voice was high and complaining. "When you are in Pisa it will be easy for you to forget that my Michelagnolo is still unable to earn his bread and your sisters are ripe for marriage. With our proud name they cannot marry into obscure families. And gentlemen of good birth will demand large dowries."

"I will provide the wedding portions when they are needed," Galileo promised recklessly.

"On your salary!" said his father.

"Perhaps I will be able to sell my next invention. And I can always instruct private pupils and earn extra fees as I have heard many of the professors do."

Still grumbling, Galileo's mother helped him pack his meager wardrobe.

"Luckily, I'll not have to spend money for fine clothes," Galileo reminded her, laughing. "My professor's gown will cover all my rags. No feasting either! I have always thrived best on bread and cheap wine. When I want an evening's pleasure, I'll play my lute. Or continue my research. You see, Father, now that I have convinced myself with the experiment with the weights I told you of—"

"If you are sensible you will spend your free time trying to earn a few more fees from your pupils," interrupted Vincenzio sharply.

At the University of Pisa the students followed the universal custom of choosing their professors for private tuition. Galileo soon found that he was anything but popular with the youths who, he had anticipated, would eke out his income with their fees for private lessons. Since books were still scarce, the students were almost entirely dependent on their professors' lectures. Galileo, without experience on the teacher's rostrum, was not a popular lecturer; he did not inspire those who heard him with the desire for study with him outside the classroom.

The antagonism the majority of the student body felt for Galileo may have been largely due to his personality. When he found a bright, inquiring mind among his pupils, he at once became the warm, sympathetic teacher. He was never too tired to explain a difficult problem, too busy with his own affairs to listen to a student's half-baked ideas. To the few congenial spirits among the student body, Galileo was actually too indulgent. He forgot the dignity of his new position and wasted evening after evening drinking with his favorites, singing improper songs and exchanging not too decorous stories.

The majority of students at Pisa—as at universities the world over—were a rowdy crew. Their wildness was encouraged by making them a privileged class and the university a privileged community beyond the regulations of the local police. This was a serious matter when boyish pranks turned into vicious lawlessness. Fortunately for Galileo's reputation he never became involved in any local scandal.

But although the professor was lenient to student rowdiness, he was anything but patient to the youths who showed themselves dull of understanding or slow to accept new ideas. They turned sullen at the sarcastic rebukes of a man hardly older than themselves—one who had never actually graduated and was held in low esteem by many of Pisa's leading professors. When Galileo returned to Pisa his welcome from the faculty was scarcely cordial. Many felt that it was not seemly that a man without a university degree should become a professor. As he was only twenty-five, his revolutionary ideas irritated the older and more conservative scholars, who believed that young men should be slow in expressing their opinions. Galileo's seniors were nearly all followers of Aristotle and the ancients; they found it more comfortable to continue in well-worn grooves. They might have forgiven Galileo for trying to think for himself, but they resented not only his iconoclastic views but the defiant manner in which he delivered them.

"If he must break idols in the market place," one of the

oldest teachers at the university complained to the rector, "need he summon all of us to see them fall and mock us when we hear them crashing to the ground?"

"He is young and foolish with a young man's pride," soothed the silver-haired rector. "I will speak to him and caution him to be more discreet."

But the rector's chiding was just what was needed to prick Galileo into action.

"I have waited too long to demonstrate to these dotards the truth I discovered for myself when I was your age," he told his few friends—all young students—as they sat over their wine cups late one night in Galileo's modest little house. "It should have convinced the most skeptical, had they seen my experiment with the two weighted chains. Yet they might have accused me of trickery, some sleight of hand to confuse them."

"But you remember, Master," one of Galileo's favorite pupils reminded him, "how to prove the truth of your hypothesis you arranged an inclined plane and bade several of us to roll down it wooden balls of unequal weight. And when the balls all reached the bottom at exactly the same time, you explained that this variation of movement, midway between the swing of the cathedral lamp and a freely falling body—"

The professor sprang to his feet and pounded on the wine-stained table.

"I have it! Tomorrow—no, day after tomorrow—no, this day a week will be best; then I shall have ample time to test my experiment in secret before I invite my witnesses. I shall invite the entire university, faculty and students, yes, and all the citizens of Pisa to watch me drop my iron weights from the top of the Leaning Tower. And all who watch shall see the two bodies striking the ground at the same moment."

"But suppose one of the iron weights strikes my unfortunate head!" gulped a student, so deep in his cups that he did not trouble to show his usual respect to his master.

"Maybe it will pound a little knowledge into your skull," answered Galileo grimly. "Now, out, all of you! And not a word of what I have told you tonight until you see the notice I shall post on the board in the central lecture hall. Then you may urge your fellows to be present. I myself shall invite the professors."

A week later, just before the stroke of noon, Galileo entered the public square. In spite of his mounting excitement, he paused as he always did to feast his beauty-loving eyes on the three splendid buildings: the cathedral, its whiteness gleaming like mountain snow in the noonday sun; the rounded Baptistery; the Leaning Tower, which though it seemed about to totter, yet remained stone-firm on its marble foundations.

At the Leaning Tower's base stood a goodly group of students, talking and laughing as boisterously as though they had gathered for an exhibition of fighting cocks, rather than a sober scientific demonstration. Of course, the rector and a number of the older members of the faculty had not demeaned themselves by coming. But here and there Galileo spied a professor, some looking highly scornful of the undignified business about to begin, others merely bored. Priests, too. "Excellent!" jubilated Galileo. "There are some excellent scientists among the Jesuits. Now if one carries word of my triumph to Rome . . . !" And, of course, the usual idlers always attracted by a gathering in a public place. While on the very edge of the crowd several beshawled old women, about to enter the cathedral, lingered, demanding to know what spectacle was to be presented and when it would begin.

Near the entrance of the Leaning Tower one of the older

professors conversed earnestly with a much younger colleague. They broke off, as though embarrassed, as Galileo approached.

"We were just debating," the older man told Galileo, hesitating a little, "whether it is wise to make such a public demonstration. If it fails—"

"It will not fail," answered Galileo sharply. He turned to speak to two of his most trusted students who waited at the door of the tower, each holding an hourglass.

Galileo repeated his instructions to the two young men. He told them where to stand that they might be sure to catch his signal from the top of the tower. Then, turning to the crowd, many of whom now murmured with impatience, he briefly outlined the purpose of his experiment.

"In my left hand," Galileo said, "see, I hold this small iron ball. It weighs exactly one pound. In my right hand, this iron ball which weighs ten pounds. If anyone wishes, he may come forward and examine them to see how greatly they differ in weight. You who are scholars have been taught Aristotle's statement that falling bodies of unequal weight, if dropped from the same height at the same moment, will reach the ground at different periods."

"Yes," a professor challenged angrily from the edge of the crowd, "and the heavier body travels in proportion to its weight. The larger ball will move through the air ten times faster than the one you hold in your left hand."

"Now keep your eyes upon me," Galileo continued as though he had not heard the heated interruption. In growing interest his listeners pressed closer. "You will see me lean over the rail above you and raise both arms as a signal to my two young friends here below that I am about to drop these balls. The hourglasses will be so adjusted that they will exactly measure the time consumed before these balls reach the ground.

"And for your own safety," he warned, "all of you stand farther back; although I shall seek to drop these weights so straight that no one will be hurt."

As he turned to enter the tower the bells clanged the hour of noon. When their pealing was ended utter silence hung over the Campo Santo as though only the dead who slept there in soil brought from the Holy Land waited for Galileo to reappear. At last the spectators standing at a safe distance from the tower saw the scientist's head and shoulders rising above the marble coping above them. The long sleeves of his scholar's gown waved in the breeze as he raised his two arms in the agreed signal. Then the two balls fell from the tower's height. They struck the ground, scattering the loose dust by their impact.

The silence was pierced by the shrill voices of the two youths who held the hourglasses: "The same time, Master! Master, there is not a second's difference!"

The crowd began to chatter as noisily as the swallows when they came to nest in the lofty belfry at eventide. "The two balls struck the earth at the same time!" "The identical time." "So you trust your eyes?" "But an hourglass does not lie." "Yes, but if there were some trickery. . . ."

Before Galileo could reach the foot of the tower nearly all those who had gathered there had drifted away. Some circled about a little girl who had raised her ragged skirts to her knees and, hoping for a few pennies, danced and sang. The crones pulled their shawls over their heads and toddled toward the cathedral, one of them complaining loudly that she had worn out her poor old legs, standing waiting to see nothing happen. Galileo looked in vain for his fellow professors. They had not stayed to congratulate him. Did they fear that his triumph might further anger those who hated him? Did they hesitate to be counted among his supporters?

But the two students who had timed the experiment stood waiting to grasp his hand.

"Master," said the younger, who had learned his manners in a prince's court, "Master, I am honored to be the first to felicitate you on your triumph."

Have I triumphed, or have I lost? thought Galileo as he smiled his thanks.

BEYOND THE DARK—THE STARS!

GALILEO, EVEN IN his hour of triumph, had every reason for his gloomy forebodings. His demonstration was denounced by the authorities as sheer pretension unworthy of a member of the faculty. A university professor playing with balls and performing tricks like a juggler at a fair! "Aristotle has said!" the professors intoned to silence the students who reported the scene at the Leaning Tower. Galileo's few friends, though they might be convinced, did not dare to defend him.

The rector called Galileo before him and again denounced his rebellion. The old man looked stern and formidable in the dark robes and fur-trimmed hood of his office.

"You have merited dismissal," he declared. "You were engaged by this university to teach old and sacred truths, not to unsettle the minds of our students by advocating your wild ideas. It is better that you leave us before you cause any more dissension."

"Why not give me the real reason why I am dismissed?" cried Galileo. "You have condemned me not only because I have uncovered errors in Aristotle. Do you think I have not heard whispers that Prince Giovanni desires my ruin?"

"I will not stoop to wrangle with you," answered the rector coldly. He knew he wasted his breath denying what had long been common gossip in Pisa.

A short time before, the grand duke's half brother had sent word to Galileo that he had completed the model of his dredging machine and desired the professor to inspect it. Those better acquainted with the amateur scientist warned Galileo that if he found anything to criticize he must be very tactful. But Galileo had never learned the meaning of tact, though he had enough worldly wisdom to realize that the Medici, if properly flattered, might prove a useful patron. On the other hand, if displeased, the royal inventor might turn into a dangerous enemy. After making a careful study of the model, Galileo declared with insulting bluntness his conscientious opinion that the proposed machine would prove worthless.

Giovanni was furious. To show his contempt for Galileo's judgment he at once gave orders to have the machine constructed along the lines of the criticized model. The prince was even more resentful when his expensive invention was completed and proved an utter failure. In his humiliation he hated the fearless professor more than ever; he openly boasted that he would never be satisfied until Galileo was dismissed. The incident of the Leaning Tower made it possible for the university to please its powerful patron.

It was hard for Galileo to leave Pisa, despised and defeated. More than his pride suffered. He had not managed to save a florin during his professorship. Vincenzio Gallilei had just died; no one expected the still immature Michelagnolo to support his widowed mother. There was no future for the sisters Livia and Virginia but the life of a nun or marriage. Neither girl felt the call to become a religious, so Galileo had promised them ample dowries. But now he not only was penniless but seemed unlikely, after the stormy years at Pisa, to find another university position.

The post of professor of mathematics at the University of Padua was vacant. When several influential friends wrote Galileo, urging him to send in his application and promising to work in his behalf, he shrank from facing further disappointment. His heart heavy with uncertainty, Galileo finally decided to journey to Venice. Here he would meet many of the mighty ones who governed the affairs of the university at Padua.

He remembered heavily those shameful, youthful years in Florence, the doors that were slammed in his face while he sought a patron, the bitterness of a dependent's bread. But he cheered himself with the thought that although he was out of favor with the faculty of Pisa, at least by now every prominent scientist in Italy had heard his name and many scholars watched his career with growing interest.

Italy was at that time divided into a number of city states. Florence ruled Pisa and dictated many of the policies of its university. The Republic of Venice governed Padua. Some of the greatest savants were eager to teach at its university, where they could enjoy the freedom of thought and speech so often denied at other centers of learning.

The same intellectual freedom also prevailed in Venice, the paradise of scholars. Its ruler, the doge, its noble families and merchant princes cultivated the arts and sciences. In their many-colored palaces which lined the twisting canals, these gentlemen had gathered not only treasures of crystal and gold and classical and contemporary works of art, but some of Europe's largest and most carefully selected libraries.

Nightly the pleasure-loving Venetians gave sumptuous feasts enlivened by masques and music; but there was always opportunity for talk of what was new in art or literature or science, as the guests lingered about the sparkling tables. Now Galileo no longer sat "below the salt." He might wear a shabby coat and wonder how he could afford to pay for his humble lodging; yet guests with jewels gleaming among the rare laces at their wrists and throats listened attentively as he told of his hydraulic scales or described his demonstrations at the Leaning Tower. Somehow Galileo had learned to speak with assurance. Over their wine goblets his ever-enlarging circle of admirers asked each other whether the newcomer, although still in his twenties, should not be considered to fill the post he sought at Padua.

It was at one of these feasts that Galileo first saw Marina Gamba and, seeing her, loved her. She wore the white veil the law permitted only to virtuous women; but it was rumored that her character hardly equaled her wit and beauty. She came from an obscure family but her humble birth was forgotten by all who came under the charm of her gracious manners and ready laughter.

Galileo discovered her name and where she dwelt. The next day he visited her, bringing a basket of fruit and flowers as his tribute. Years later, when those early days in Venice faded into a dream of blue waters and cloudless skies, he still could clearly picture Marina Gamba glowing with the splendor of her first youth. The noonday sun, forcing its way between the broken lattice, shone hotly on her black hair and the apricot she pressed to her full lips. He noticed that her hands were very small for a woman so tall and stately.

They were beautiful hands and he would never allow her to

deface them with rings. But he was not a miserly lover. Securing a loan from one of his new friends, Galileo hurried to a goldsmith on the Rialto and bought her a pair of earrings that jingled sweetly when she walked; his second gift was a necklace of tiny stones, blue, crimson and orange, set in a curious mosaic design.

"Do not buy me any more presents, Galileo Galilei," he remembered her saying. "I know that whenever you bring me a gift you must go hungry. Let other men buy me trinkets. From you I want only your songs."

Then he would take out his lute and play for her as they sat on the balcony of her little house. Sometimes he would sing verses he had made for her sake. More often he repeated to his lute's accompaniment what had become her favorite, snatches from a poem another Italian lover had fashioned for his lady over four centuries before:

> I have sought through Calabria,
>   Lombardy, and Tuscany,
> Rome, Pisa, Lucca, Genoa,
>   All between sea and sea:
> Yea, even to Babylon I went
>   And distant Barbary:
> But not a woman found I anywhere
> Equal to thee, who are indeed most fair.

Glancing down the narrow canal, Galileo smiled to see a gondola heaped high with many-colored flowers for the market. He threw a coin to the gondolier who flung a handful of roses and jasmine to Marina Gamba as he passed. Galileo had never been so happy.

They rejoiced together when Galileo received his appointment as professor of mathematics at Padua. Marina promised to follow him as soon as he had established himself at the university and could settle her in a house of her own. It is likely that only Galileo's pride in his lineage kept him from offering her marriage.

Since the salary Galileo was promised at Padua was half as much again as he had received at Pisa, he was foolish enough to hope that his financial troubles were over. But he still found the family he had left in Florence far too costly for his means. He felt honor bound to pay the debts his father had incurred during his last miserable years. There was a monthly sum to be set aside for his mother and a smaller but regular amount to be sent to pay for Livia's board and tuition in a convent. Livia was jealous that her sister Virginia was already married. To quiet the younger girl's impatience, Galileo wrote his mother, "Tell her there have been queens and great ladies who have not married till they are old enough to be her mother."

Virginia's marriage had already cost her older brother many a sleepless night. Her bridegroom, the son of a Florentine official, was almost as poor as she, but demanded a marriage portion commensurate with his family's position. Galileo had promised in writing to pay the marriage portion within a certain period after the wedding. For some unaccountable reason he felt more secure when Michelagnolo signed the document.

He should have known that his young brother was as unreliable and lazy as he was talented. When the boy quarreled with his mother he came to live with Galileo in Padua, promising to support himself by giving lessons on the lute. But he made no effort to find pupils and the few who came seldom found their teacher waiting for them, since Michelagnolo liked to escape his one obligation by frequenting the nearest tavern. Galileo, although he was deep in debt, was glad to get rid of him by advancing enough gold to send him to Poland. Here for some years Michelagnolo earned his own living as a court musician.

Rid of this nuisance, the easygoing older brother faced a new calamity. Growing impatient, Virginia's husband threatened a lawsuit. Galileo shrank from exposing his mother and sisters to such shame. Worse, even if he could not be extradited from Padua he would surely be thrown into prison for debt if he ever returned to Florence. In desperation, Galileo wrote to his brother, reminding the musician that he had also signed the marriage document and should feel obligated to pay his share.

Michelagnolo answered that he had just married and that the wedding feast had been a great expense. He boasted that among the eighty distinguished guests there were actually four ambassadors. He had felt that there was no reason to postpone his own marriage in order "to save a few miserable farthings" to placate his brother-in-law. "I am more than certain that in thirty years I should not have saved enough to cover this debt," he airily waved aside his obligation.

Galileo told Marina that he wished he had strangled his lute-playing relative in his cradle. Then, humbling himself, he borrowed an advance on his salary for the next two years and sent the money to Virginia's bridegroom.

The marriages in my family are too costly—for me, he decided grimly, glad that—as at Pisa—he might earn an extra sum by private tutoring. But with this addition to his income, he felt he could not refuse to dower his sister Livia. She had grown tired of her convent school, returned to her mother and shortly afterward wrote her indulgent brother of her betrothal.

Since her lover came from a noble Florentine family, she argued, she should receive a more substantial marriage portion than her sister.

Galileo wearily agreed. Later, in the handwriting which was to record the greatest discoveries of his age, he noted down a list of articles he had purchased for the bride: a bed with silken curtains; dresses of velvet and damask; a pair of high shoes. Remembering the poverty of his own boyhood, Galileo did not want her to feel ashamed before her new relatives.

He was just as prodigal in the management of his own affairs. Besides his salary he not only received his pupils' private fees, but payment for board and lodgings from those who lived in his house. But it is doubtful whether for all his knowledge of mathematics the professor ever was able to balance his accounts. He was too easygoing to check the purchases made by a dishonest housekeeper; too kindly to demand payment from a careless or indigent lodger.

Meanwhile his own expenses mounted year by year. He maintained a separate household for Marina Gamba, who bore him three children. The two pretty little daughters he named after his own troublesome sisters. He could imagine how proud his father would have been of his first grandson and namesake.

Galileo's health during these years in Padua became of greater concern than even his many debts and obligations. He began to suffer severely from arthritis, which at intervals left him crippled and bedridden. Marina sometimes offered to nurse him, but he preferred a servant. He was proud; he did not want her—younger than he and still so beautiful and strong—to see him changed temporarily into a crippled, prematurely old man, twisting and moaning with pain.

Yet in spite of these nagging demands upon his purse and

energy, Galileo grew to love Padua with a deep and abiding love. Shortly before his death under circumstances he had never dreamed of during his honored and busy sojourn in the picturesque university town, Galileo wrote wistfully to a friend: "It is not without envy that I learn of your return to Padua, where I spent the eighteen best years of my life. Enjoy to the utmost the liberty and friendships which I appreciated so deeply myself—both at Padua and in the neighboring city of Venice."

In his new loyalty to Padua Galileo could never forswear his admiration for Florence in all her remembered loveliness. But he realized that Padua, although so different, also possessed a unique grandeur. Here instead of the fortresslike palaces of the Renaissance he found architecture built under Gothic influence. The substantial comfortable houses were joined together by arcades; the roofs which almost met overhead furnished protection from the rains of autumn and winter, the summer's sun. Here on the benches before the many bookstores and shops a man might see and gossip with his fellow professors or listen to the latest news from abroad. Merchants who had visited the great fairs in France and Germany often brought back not only goods but newly printed books and thought-provoking ideas gathered in far places.

The focus of Padua's intellectual life, its university, was one of the world's greatest centers of learning of that period. Many of the famed universities had been an outgrowth of the cloister and cathedral schools. But the University of Padua, which began with its law school, was due to what may be termed a scholars' "strike." Early in the thirteenth century Bologna, like every other university town of the period, depended for its prosperity largely on the community of students and teachers who had come to study within its gates. Knowing this, the university group often grew rather overbearing in its demands. A violent quarrel arose in Bologna between town and gown. The professors in their long gowns and flat caps called their black-robed students together and marched off to Padua to found a new school there.

Here canon—or church law—and civil law were taught. Gradually other branches like medicine and philosophy were added. Because of the freedom of thought and expression not only tolerated but welcomed at Padua, its courses in science grew and flourished. The professor of mathematics, whose death led to Galileo's appointment, had been renowned through Europe.

After the Cathedral of St. Anthony, the most important structure in Padua was the university's headquarters. It was known as the Bo, because the picture of an ox, painted while the building was used as an inn, still decorated the great middle door. The university men called themselves Bovists; like students the world over they were extremely jealous of their rights and ready to fight for their traditions.

The Bovists carried on a bitter feud with the Jesuits, who many years after the founding of the university had come to Padua to establish a school of their own. When the newcomers declared they had the right to ring a certain brazen bell to announce their classes, there were actually fights between the students of the Bo and of the Jesuit College. The university professors, as befitted their dignity, fought with their pens instead of their fists; in their polemics they defended their teaching and criticized the Jesuits and many of their ideas. The Jesuits, on the other hand, accused the university faculty of spreading falsehood and heresy.

For once Galileo did not enter the controversy. He knew

that many of the Jesuits were learned and conscientious and tolerant of new ideas; he could never forget the understanding and kindness Father Clavius of the Roman College had once shown an obscure and struggling student.

Among the university faculty there were many scholars ready to listen to criticism of Aristotle. Perhaps the freedom of thought permitted at Padua pacified Galileo, who had left his youthful rebellion far behind. Although he had never fought authority merely for the joy of battle, when in doubt he had asked Why? and had tried to solve the problem which confronted him. And, Galileo decided, there were more important things for a good Catholic to do than to argue against the doctrines which St. Thomas Aquinas had reconciled with the teachings of the Church.

One morning, during his first months at Padua, Galileo stood in the Santo admiring the great altar Donatello had carved for the greater glory of St. Anthony. How long ago it seemed when he, a hot-tempered student, had lingered in the cathedral at Pisa and watched a lamp swaying in the dusk! But now he thought less of Aristotle than of the Angelic Doctor, Aquinas, considered by many the greatest theologian of the Church.

Galileo reverently recalled the dying words of the Dominican scholar: "For Thee have I studied, watched and labored. Thee have I preached. Thee have I taught. Against Thee I have never spoken. Neither am I wedded to my own opinion. If I have held anything which is untrue, I subject it to the judgment of the Holy Roman Church, in whose obedience I now pass from this life."

Moved by such saintly humility, Galileo prayed that he, too, might make so good an end.

Even if Galileo had desired to engage in disputations during his first years in Padua, he was far too busy. He slaved over his lectures which from his first in 1592 were immensely popular. Now he no longer feared to face hostile faces or empty benches in the lecture room. The students who enjoyed his lively presentations told their friends; soon the great hall became crowded with young men who came early that they might jostle their way to a favorable spot near the lectern. Success made Galileo even more successful. He became so skillful in presenting his material that many students, although not especially interested in the subjects, were eager to hear his fresh and inspiring talks on mathematics, physics and astronomy. Years later one of his former pupils, Professor Marsalio of Padua, declared: "I learned more from Galileo in three months than in as many years from other men."

His instruction on military attack and defense, based on scientific principles, proved most valuable to the young noblemen, who came to the university from every part of Italy and in some cases from other European countries. For this was a science which they might someday need in protecting their estates. Sometimes Galileo wondered why men were so obsessed with the means of destroying their enemies. Much more, he reflected sadly, than in his discovery of a method of irrigation which would mean more food for hungry peasants! He could not foresee that he would soon begin what would prove the greatest work of his career because certain rulers were eager to possess an instrument useful for warfare.

The circle of Galileo's private pupils grew larger every month. Many of them lodged in his house and Galileo became not only their teacher but their friend. He enjoyed his daily close contact with eager young minds; as he had never left Italy, Galileo made the most of this opportunity of knowing intimately youths from France and Sweden and Germany. So great was the liberality of Catholic Padua that it welcomed to its university scholars from even the strongholds of Lutheran opposition. Galileo, being equally tolerant, drew no distinction between Catholic and Protestant, but treated every member of his large household like an understanding father.

Some of the youths who came from afar knew little Italian, so Latin in many and often weird dialects was spoken around the long dinner table. Often at meals the discussion was devoted to the day's studies; but more frequently Galileo, enthroned in the great chair at the head of the table, persuaded a foreign student to describe his own university, or questioned another on the politics and social customs of his native country.

Students favored to live under Galileo's roof never forgot these enlightening table talks. For years after leaving Padua many of them corresponded with their old master. Those who continued their scientific studies kept in touch with Galileo to discuss their work. Some who came from noble families connected with Italian rulers or the papal court were to use their influence when the beloved professor faced shame and suffering.

A consecrated teacher, Galileo rejoiced that his influence on his pupils spanned an ever-increasing circle like those which widen about a pebble thrown into the water. Not only the twenty-odd students who shared his lark pie and salad at the noisy table were helped and inspired. He was the mentor of those who lingered after his lectures to ask questions, who pushed back their wine cups in the tavern to listen to his stories. Galileo felt certain that these laughing, eager boys from France, these slow, methodical thinkers from Germany and the Low Countries would carry back something of their master when they returned to their native lands.

Having known bitter poverty during his own student days, the Paduan professor was always ready to lend a helping hand to the youths who struggled and starved on a scanty stipend. He smiled grimly at the tale of the three students who lived together in uncomplaining poverty until they were questioned for attending only one lecture out of three. Then the authorities learned that the trio had only one *cappa* between them; each in turn had worn the gown while the other two huddled over the brazier in their garret and shivered in their scanty rags.

Many of the student body came from families with moderate means and lived comfortably enough in a boardinghouse like Galileo's. Other students were of noble or royal birth and at Padua continued to enjoy the luxuries they had known at home. These lodged in palaces, surrounded by a miniature court: young noblemen whom they had known since childhood; private chaplains and tutors; servants ranging from valets to cooks. Galileo remembered not only his early poverty but also that he had sprung from a family not unacquainted with courts. He mingled easily with the young aristocrats, showing them the same friendship—no more, no less—that he felt for the poorest student, grateful for a full meal or a pair of shoes.

Perhaps Galileo enjoyed—even more than his contacts with the student body—the hours he spent with his fellow professors and a group of patrons of learning both in Padua and Venice. In this group one of Galileo's earliest friends and admirers was Giovan Vincenzio Pinelli.

Pinelli was a shining example of the men of wealth of that period, who not only achieved fame as a friend of learning but continued his own studies. When his student days at the University of Padua ended, he began his collection of rare books and manuscripts until the library of his magnificent home

housed eighty thousand volumes. He was often the host of
princes and cardinals, artists and writers. Professors from the
university sometimes brought a few fortunate pupils to one of
Pinelli's evening parties, where the other guests were permitted
to listen to their discussions on many subjects.

Then, if the arguments grew too long or too heated, Pinelli
would be induced to perform upon his lyre. As Galileo never
lost his interest in music, it is likely that he was persuaded to
accompany his friend on the lute. A feast followed the music.
Flushed with wine, Galileo sauntered homeward, singing as
lustily as any of the students who walked beside him.

The friend of many prominent European scientists, Pinelli
often corresponded with Tycho Brahe, who has been called
the "oracle of mathematical science." Galileo was eager to
discuss a number of still unsolved problems with Brahe and
was grateful when Pinelli mentioned his name to the Danish
mathematician and astronomer and suggested that Galileo should
write to the older scientist. The Paduan professor's letter remained unanswered for eight years. Always cold and withdrawn, it is likely that the famous scholar did not care to waste
his time writing to a professor still unknown beyond the borders
of Italy. It was not until the year of his death that Tycho Brahe
decided that Galileo's rising fame merited his attention.

Such pride was foreign to Galileo's generous nature. When
Johannes Kepler, the German astronomer who became Brahe's
successor, published his first book, Galileo wrote the young
and long-unrecognized genius a letter of heart-warming praise.
Although they never met, the two scientists became warm
friends; they were drawn together largely through their mutual
admiration of Copernicus.

For it happened that during the early years of his professorship at Padua Galileo had run across the almost forgotten book a churchman had written while serving his obscure parish in Germany. Who was this Copernicus who had set down such startling theories based on his lifelong astronomical studies? Galileo had heard that the neglected scientist had once attended classes at Padua. The professor burrowed in the university archives until he found the name registered in the roll books. Galileo felt strangely proud and happy that Copernicus, whom he was beginning to admire so fervently, had been a student at Padua a century before.

So Galileo continued to study and to write, to lecture, to attend banquets in Padua and Venice where he might relax during an evening of masque and music. But the diversion he most enjoyed was tinkering, as his father called it, at his work-table. Many of the inventions remained unfinished. But one, a greatly improved compass to be used in mechanical drawing, brought the inventor considerable revenue and soon began to add to his growing reputation.

Galileo constructed this instrument by crossing two metal rulers which were fastened together diagonally by a graduated scale. By adjusting the angles of the two rulers according to the scale, the instrument might be used to enlarge a map or drawing. Soon this compass was in such demand that Galileo hired a workman to construct copies of the original model. That the mechanic might work under his direction, Galileo invited him to come to live under his roof. The workman brought his family with him. Now when Galileo's sisters and their children or the aging, quarrelsome mother came to visit him, the big house seemed overcrowded and noisy.

But Galileo would laughingly shut himself in his study to read; or to take notes on what he had just read; or to write lengthy letters, adorned with carefully polished phrases, to his many correspondents. Sometimes if the night were fine and his arthritis did not trouble him, he would sit in the garden in quiet meditation. God has been very good to me, he thought. . . . After wandering so long like Dante through bewildering terrors and uncertainties, like his beloved poet he was able to glimpse at last the reassurance of the stars.

NEW STARS IN THE HEAVENS

IN THE YEAR 1604 a new star of exceeding brilliance brightened the autumnal skies.

Johannes Kepler made an exhaustive study of the strange star which came to be known by his name. Galileo Galilei gave three lectures upon it. Astronomers everywhere discussed the phenomenon. For it was generally believed that the number of the stars had never varied since the Creation. A new star had no place in the picture of a completed universe accepted by believers in the scriptures or by Aristotle. It seemed logical for the astrologers to hail the apparition as the forerunner of strange and terrible events.

Everyone in Padua wondered; many grew sick with fear. Being Christians, the folk at Padua no longer worshiped the sun and the moon after the fashion of their pagan ancestors. But many believed that the stars controlled the affairs of men. In the stars the astrologers read the most fortunate season for the navigator to set out to sea, for the general to lead his army into battle. The peasant sowed his grain, his prince signed a treaty with a foreign power—if the stars were declared favorable to such undertakings.

At the beginning of every year almanacs were published showing the position of the planets in the forthcoming months and gravely describing their effects on mankind. A century before Galileo, the French friar Rabelais had satirized such predictions by writing: "This year the stone-blind shall see but little; the deaf shall hear but scurvily; the dumb shall not speak very plain; the rich shall be in somewhat better circumstances than the poor, and the healthy than the sick. . . . The ruler of the year is neither Saturn, Mars, nor Jupiter, but God the Creator . . . by reason of eclipses crabs will move sideways; also a horrible malady will be everywhere—that is lack of money."

Many readers laughed at his mockery—then returned with implicit faith to their almanacs.

Not only in Catholic France and Italy but in Protestant England men trembled before the power of the heavenly bodies. Shakespeare, a contemporary of Galileo, might scoff at such vulgar supersition and declare:

> "The fault, dear Brutus, is not in our stars,
> But in ourselves, that we are underlings."

but his audience, from the sweaty, illiterate groundlings to the gentlemen scholars just come down from Oxford, brushed aside such heresy. They knew a man's fortune, good or evil, lay in the influence of the star under which he was born. And more, one of the learned might add, the destiny of an entire nation was swayed by the heavenly bodies.

A historian might recall that in 1572 a star, so bright that it dimmed its neighbors and was visible even in daylight, had appeared as the forerunnner of the Massacre of St. Bartholomew in Paris. Could this star of evil omen have been sent to predict the end of the world? terrified Frenchmen asked each other, while the waters of the Seine reddened with blood. Nor did fears lessen when an astrologer spoke of the comet of 1456. In that year the pope, Calixtus III, had decreed that every Christian should pray for protection against the blazing visitor as well as the military power of the heathen Turks. But the Turks had been defeated and the sun still continued to revolve around the earth—as taught by Aristotle and believed by all but a few crackbrained astronomers like Copernicus.

Shortly after his arrival in Padua, Galileo had added astronomy to his many interests. Like all astronomers before the day of the telescope, he was forced to confine his searchings in the heavens to the bodies visible to the naked eye. Reading in the rich libraries of Venice and Padua, he grew greatly excited over the theory of Copernicus, who had been discredited by churchmen and scholars. But Galileo, after much pondering, wrote to the astronomer Kepler: "I have become a convert to the opinions of Copernicus and by his theory have succeeded in explaining many phenomena which on the contrary hypothesis are altogether inexplicable."

Who was this scientist who was to change not only the life of Galileo but through him the opinions of every astronomer for centuries to come?

Nikolaus Copernicus is claimed by both Germans and Poles. It is likely he was descended from a German family who had migrated a century earlier from what is now Germany into Poland; he was born in 1473, at Thorn on the Vistula. He belonged to the period of the great discoverers—Columbus,

Vasco da Gama and Magellan. But instead of seeking shorter paths to the treasure lands of gold and spice, he devoted his life to mapping the still uncharted expanses of the heavens.

After Copernicus had specialized for three years in mathematics and astronomy at the University of Cracow, his uncle, the bishop of Frauenburg, Germany, sent him to Italy to continue his studies. At the University of Bologna he studied Greek and philosophy; here he met the astronomer Domineco da Novara, who taught him what European scientists were just beginning to learn—the art of observation.

It is likely that through his readings in Plato, Copernicus learned at this time of the theory of the earlier Greeks, especially Pythagoras. Certain philosophers before Aristotle believed not only that the earth was round, not flat, but that it moved around the sun. This theory was contradicted by the omnipotent Aristotle and by Claudius Ptolemy, who studied the stars over Alexandria during the earlier half of the first century of the Christian Era.

This Egyptian scientist and author continued to rule the minds of scholars until the Renaissance. Then the revival of interest in Greek introduced Plato to men like Novara who became somewhat skeptical concerning the Ptolemaic system. But the majority of Christian scholars still accepted the belief which made our earth the center of the universe. They read in Holy Writ—together with other proofs—that Joshua had bade the sun and moon to stand still while he battled against the enemies of Israel. Only a madman or a heretic seeking to destroy the authority of the Church could doubt such evidence!

After completing his studies at Bologna Copernicus visited Rome, where he gave a series of lectures on mathematics. Later he studied both law and medicine at the University of Padua.

Like Galileo he had many interests; unlike the Italian, who was to become his stoutest champion, Copernicus was always a conscientious student and became an excellent physician.

Now his uncle, the bishop, who had long ago decided that Copernicus should take holy orders, had the young man appointed as canon at Frauenburg. He remained in this parish on the border of East Prussia until his death thirty-seven years later, ministering to both the souls and bodies of his congregants.

The records of the ancient cathedral tell of baptisms, of marriages and of burials he performed. His scientific mind rebelled against many of the crude practices of his day. He would advise a frantic mother that instead of accusing a neighbor of bewitching her sick child, she would be wiser to keep it clean and give it wholesome food. He suggested a simple remedy to cure the colic of the babe he had just baptized. When called to hear the last confession of a parishioner, the canon always sought to relieve the dying man's physical agony. His poor patients whom he served only for love believed he was the wisest doctor in all Germany. This opinion was shared by the bishops Copernicus attended and by certain noblemen like Duke Albert of Prussia.

Although he never neglected his many duties, the greatest interest of his life remained astronomy. Night after night he studied the skies and made his calculations with the rude instruments of that period—noting down his calculations one evening, only to change them when they could not be verified. He never forgot his early studies with Novara. All that he had learned and observed led him to record: "The idea came to me that Ptolemy's fundamental postulate was wrong, and that the earth instead of being the pivot of the entire universe, as Ptolemy thought it was, is merely one planet among others revolving around the sun."

So he wrote one night in his little tower bedroom after he had completed a long day filled with duties as canon and physician. On this idea he continued to ponder for thirty years.

Little by little Copernicus' daring views became known in academic circles. One of his friends persuaded him to write a brief sketch of his ideas; it was privately circulated in manuscript form. In 1533 a German scholar brought a verbal account of the canon's hypothesis to the pope, Clement VII. Several years later the Archbishop of Capua, a close friend to the Pope, advised Copernicus to make his theory known to the world.

By this time Copernicus had completed his book, *The Revolution of the Heavenly Bodies*. But as Copernicus knew that the liberal views of Pope Clement did not represent the Church as a whole, he still hesitated to publish his work. A few years later Professor Georg Joachim Rheticus left his duties in Wittenberg, the center of Protestant learning, to visit Copernicus. Both scientists were deeply religious. But being true scientists they forgot their religious differences, in spite of the cruel hatred which existed between Catholic and Protestant. They became devoted friends. At last Rheticus persuaded the hesitating priest to have the book printed. It was published in Nürnberg in 1543, just in time for an advance copy to reach Copernicus on his deathbed.

Suffering from hemorrhage and paralysis, Copernicus, who had lingered on after his seventieth birthday, asked a fellow priest to place the heavy volume upon his pillow. The May sun shone brightly through the many-paned window; its warm rays gilded the weary, white head and the book which was to give a new universe to mankind. Contented, the canon closed his eyes and drifted into sleep.

For a short time *The Revolution of the Heavenly Bodies* was read and vehemently discussed by the leading scientists of Europe. Copernicus had been cautious in expressing his views, many of which agreed with Ptolemy's. But by the fifth chapter he considered the possibility that the earth might have a circular motion of its own. Several chapters later his readers found him stating that "nothing stands in the way of the movability of the earth." He boldly affirmed that he regarded the earth as one of the planets, declaring: "One shall be convinced that the Sun itself occupies the center of the Universe."

Churchmen and schoolmen of the universities of Oxford, of Paris, of Padua thumped their ink-stained desks as they argued late into the night. Often when the heated discussions were over, the disputants would reach for their pens and repeat the evening's arguments to some faraway fellow scientist.

It was all so very puzzling! This theory had not been propounded by a rebel against the Church; its author had lived and died a faithful, obedient believer. He had actually dedicated this most disturbing book to the Pope! Although, hinted some cynics, this courtesy might have risen less out of respect for His Holiness than the desire to win protection for the author and his work.

Many Protestant and Catholic scholars forgot their theological differences long enough to agree that this new theory was not only ridiculous but blasphemous. It contradicted the teachings of Holy Writ; more, by reducing the earth to a mere planet revolving with others around the sovereign sun, it lowered the dignity of man, who had hitherto occupied this globe as the highest of all God's creatures!

Some scholars were not particularly interested in theological problems. But like unlearned and simple people they, too, had their deeply rooted beliefs which they were reluctant to abandon. The judges who doomed Socrates to drink the deadly hemlock were probably honest men, fearful of changes his radical ideas on religion and politics might bring to Athens. Many of the scientists who opposed the discoveries of Pasteur—or Einstein's theory of relativity—also were merely suspicious of new ideas.

The excitement soon died down and Copernicus and his book were forgotten. Here and there scholars like Galileo might ponder over a theory acceptable to their reason but impossible to prove. For even Tycho Brahe, an older contemporary of the professor of Padua, and the greatest mathematician of his time, found it unacceptable. A strange paradox! For this famous Dane, although a strong opponent of the Copernican theory, was by his mathematical contributions the first scientist to establish it firmly for later scholars.

Tycho Brahe was born into an aristocratic family in southern Sweden, which in the year 1546 was still Danish territory. Educated by private tutors, he entered the University of Copenhagen at the age of twelve, studying rhetoric and philosophy and preparing himself for a diplomatic career.

Here in 1560 an eclipse of the sun stirred the young student so deeply that he turned to what was to become his lifework, mathematics and astronomy. He was greatly stirred that the eclipse had taken place at approximately the predicted time. [There is] "something divine," he wrote, "that men should know the motions of the stars so accurately that they could long before foretell their places and relative positions." "Could not the rough tables of these computations be further improved?" he asked himself and began feverishly to study both mathematics and astronomy.

After three years, he left Copenhagen for the University of Leipzig. Like Galileo, who in his student days neglected his medical classes for mathematics, Tycho Brahe refused to prepare for a career in which he was not interested. Although Tycho's family ordered his tutor to keep the youth at his law courses, the young Dane continued to devote his time to science.

He refused to accept the theories he found in the now neglected writings of Copernicus, yet the restless-minded student became convinced that the only way to decide which system of the universe was correct was to follow the methods of the astronomer-priest. Brahe decided that he, too, would devote his life to practical observation.

Tycho Brahe found that astronomy was still as hidebound and encrusted with superstition as medicine. Even this brilliant thinker, while a student, seems to have believed in astrology; at least he is known to have drawn up horoscopes for his friends! Instruments like the compass and the cross-staff were still crude and undeveloped. When in 1565 he returned home to Denmark, of course his family vehemently opposed his plans for a scientific career.

Undaunted, Tycho Brahe continued his studies. For some unknown reason he took up chemistry. As the terms "chemistry" and "alchemy" were still interchangeable in those days, he may well have devoted his time to trying to discover the secret of turning baser metals into gold. Fortunately for astronomical research and for the disappointed chemist's financial security, his father's death left him in possession of a considerable legacy. There was no longer any pressure to delay work in the field he had chosen for himself.

His old interest in astronomy flamed into life again when, in September, 1572, he was startled to see a very bright star in the constellation Cassiopeia. "Since I had almost from boy-hood known all the stars of the heavens perfectly," he writes, "it was quite evident to me that there had never before been any star in that place in the sky, even the smallest, to say nothing of a star so conspicuously bright as this. I was so aston-ished at this sight that I was not ashamed to doubt the trust-worthiness of my own eyes."

Tycho Brahe was not the only one to see this brilliant star; but he was the only one to observe it systematically. This discovery was of great importance, since the followers of Aristotle had always maintained his belief that there could be no change in the so-called "fixed stars." Astronomers had always known that the "wandering stars," as the planets were called, constantly change their positions. For example, Jupiter is sometimes the morning, sometimes the evening, star. But the multitude of other visible stars remained fixed in their relative positions. However, now the impossible had happened. Here was a new star appearing in the familiar pattern of Cassiopeia!

Gradually the lovely visitor began to dim; by March of the following year it became invisible to the naked eye, so no one could study it further. But many confirmed Aristotelians began to wonder.

Now the king, Frederick II, offered Brahe a little island be-tween Elsinore and Landskrona where he erected an observa-tory. Here for twenty years in his City of the Heavens he ob-served the firmament and set down what he had observed.

Tycho Brahe constructed instruments remarkable for their accuracy in the days before the telescope revolutionized astron-omy. He became known chiefly for his observations of the planets. He decided that by gathering together all possible observations of the positions and motions of these bodies, he could help to settle the ever-growing question: who was right, Ptolemy or Copernicus? His earliest studies had convinced this conscientious mathematician that there were certain flaws in the Egyptian's picture of the universe. Brahe did not approve of the old system. He might have accepted the startling new ideas of Copernicus had he not felt them to be contrary to the teaching of scripture as well as impossible to prove scientifically.

In France and Italy a number of astronomers prepared to follow Tycho Brahe in discarding the discredited Ptolemaic system. But, they puzzled, had not the master of them all declared definitely that he still believed the earth was the center of the universe? There might be some truth in the hypothesis of Copernicus, said the cautious ones, but if a scholar espoused it too openly, what about the Inquisition! They knew the power of this court of inquiry, established by the Church in the thirteenth century to guide the conscience of every Catholic and to prevent him from straying from the faith.

Appointed by the emperor, Rudolph II, as imperial mathematician, Tycho Brahe spent the last years of his life in Bohemia. Grieving to leave his work unfinished, he turned on his deathbed to urge his young assistant Johannes Kepler to complete the Rudolphine tables, a most valuable recording of the planetary motions which Brahe had named to honor his patron.

"Oh, that I may not have lived in vain!" Tycho Brahe murmured in Latin again and again as his questioning mind began to wander and he felt the darkness closing in about him.

No one knew better than Tycho Brahe himself how cruelly weary he had grown night after night, seeking to read the still unsolved riddles of the heavens. Now at fifty-five he was too ill and worn to struggle any longer. He left his unpublished computations and observations, together with his instruments, to Kepler. Would Kepler make good use of his legacy as he continued his master's lifelong search for truth? Perhaps it was well that Tycho Brahe could not look down the years and foresee that his disciple by the very use of this precious inheritance would help to prove the theory which the older man had continued to deny to the end.

To become first the assistant and then the heir to the greatest mathematician of the century was one of the very few strokes of good fortune to brighten the life of Johannes Kepler. He was born in Württemberg at the time when seven-year-old Galileo had already started to plague his father with unseemly questions. Unlike the Florentine, Kepler never knew what it was to have a parent to instruct him and plan for his future. His father was a drunkard; having wasted his inheritance, he first turned soldier, then innkeeper. Kepler and his two younger brothers were taken out of school to serve as potboys, to endure the complaints of the impatient customers and the nagging Frau Kepler—from the time she set the boys to work in the morning until late at night, when they dragged their weary bodies to bed.

But by the time Kepler reached his fifteenth year, even his besotted father realized that this son was too promising to spend the rest of his life serving drinks and sweeping out the taproom. He actually allowed Johannes to attend a preparatory school. Five years later the youth received his degree of Master of Arts "with distinction" at the University of Tübingen.

But by this time the elder Kepler had deserted his wife and children. Johannes' mother, embittered by poverty, grew more and more unmanageable. It was rumored that she dealt in witchcraft and her few remaining friends began to shun the unhappy family. Kepler longed to find refuge in his studies, but they were interrupted by his uncertain health.

For a while he contemplated entering the Lutheran ministry, but he was repelled by certain dogmas which cramped his free, inquiring spirit. One belief he would have had to renounce was his faith in the Copernican theory. At the University of Tübingen one of Kepler's professors had ventured to teach that the hypothesis might prove correct; Johannes was among the first of his students to agree with him.

After his appointment as a lecturer on astronomy at the University of Grätz in Austria, Kepler at the amazing age of twenty-four published his first book. In this work on the heavenly bodies he fearlessly defended Copernicus, basing all his arguments not on theory but on observed facts. Fortunately this volume won praise from both Tycho Brahe and Galileo.

It was at this time that the professor of mathematics at Padua dared to write the younger scientist that he, too, had become a convert to the opinions of Copernicus. If the world moved, scientific knowledge also moved a little farther out of the shadows, while these two fearless men prepared to battle for what they believed.

In the same year that Kepler was cheered by the commendations of Galileo, the German astronomer made his first, and unfortunate, marriage. Kepler did not expect his bride to follow or to appreciate his work. But he had hoped she would make his life a little easier. There had been talk before the marriage of the considerable fortune the lady would bring as a dowry. But there was no dowry and, having no income but his small salary from the university, the scholar had to continue his battle against poverty.

Even this inadequate income vanished the following year.

The university which had been Protestant now came under the control of the Catholic church; all Protestant teachers were expelled. Later Kepler was invited to return. But life in an Austrian university at the beginning of the seventeenth century was greatly complicated by religious rancors. Soon every Protestant professor and assistant was informed he must either become a Catholic or leave the country within forty-five days.

Johannes Kepler deeply loved his religion, even though in his devotion to what he believed the truth he had been forced to oppose many Lutherans in the matter of the Copernican theory. It was unthinkable that he should desert his childhood faith. When almost mad with despair, he was rescued by an offer from Tycho Brahe to come to Prague as one of his three assistants.

After Brahe's death Kepler succeeded him as imperial mathematician. He held this position until the end of his life, but it brought him more honor than bread. Because of the necessities of his family, he was actually forced to demean himself by recognizing astrology, which he so greatly despised. In 1616, seeking to scrape together enough to publish his works, he bitterly declared: "I have been obliged to compose a vile, prophesying almanac, which is scarcely more respectable than begging, unless from its saving the emperor's credit, who abandons me entirely and would suffer me to perish from hunger."

His salary was paid so irregularly by his royal patron that Kepler again knew the poverty of his boyhood. His wife and one of his children died. He made a second marriage to secure someone to care for his motherless family and it was a fortunate one. But as always he could not enjoy tranquillity. His mother, now almost eighty, caused him bitter sorrow; only her death saved her from being brought before a court to face trial for witchcraft.

There followed alternate years of comfort and privation. With the salary he received as imperial mathematician he at last carried out Tycho Brahe's request and published the Rudolphine tables.

Unlike his master, Kepler made comparatively few astronomical observations since he was primarily a mathematician, not an astronomer. But he did engage in a long and intensive study of the "temporary star" which now bears his name.

Guided by the records which Tycho Brahe had bequeathed to him, Kepler, harassed by poverty and uncertainties, continued to study the laws of planetary motion. For eight years he labored on his *Commentaries on the Motions of Mars,* demonstrating the famous "Three Laws" which were named in his honor. He wrote that the laws which govern the movements of Mars would apply to other planets as well, even assuming that all the planets moved around the sun and that the moon moved around the earth.

Broken in spirit and body by his many hardships and disappointments, he still had the faith to write in one of his books what might have been chosen for his epitaph: "The die is cast, the book is written, to be read now or by posterity, I care not. I can well wait a century for a reader, since God has waited six thousand years for a discoverer."

Galileo, reading this challenge to the future, felt a strong spiritual bond with the man he had long admired for his genius and his courage. Johannes Kepler had been willing to suffer for his loyalty as a Protestant; Galileo was a devoted Catholic. Yet both men in their search for scientific truth dared to defy the persecution of the churchmen and scholars of a most intolerant era.

Galileo Galilei might have remained safe from such persecution if he had taken the advice of his friends who urged him to continue to teach and study under the liberal laws of the Venetian republic. But in spite of his success at the University of Padua, and the countless friends he had made both there and in Venice, his heart often yearned for Florence and he grew homesick for the city of his youth.

THE GRAND DUKE OF TUSCANY
REMEMBERS GALILEO

GALILEO'S FORTUNE CONTINUED to ascend with the rising of the strange new star in 1604. So many listeners—not only students at the university but eminent visitors to Padua—crowded to hear his lectures that a larger hall was needed.

Accounts of the compass he had invented also increased the professor's fame. It was found extremely useful in plotting military operations. Since it was necessary to know geometry to understand its use, those who were interested in the instrument came to Galileo to have him teach them how to employ it. Many aristocratic amateurs were intrigued by such inventions as toys rather than practical aids in mathematics and mechanics. More than one prince sent to Padua for the "miraculous compass" and later turned to his helpless court mathematician to explain its use.

It happened that among the many high-born youths who came to Galileo for private instruction was young Nicolo Giugni, son of the grand chamberlain of the Tuscan court. Returning to Florence, Nicolo spoke with enthusiasm of Gali-

leo—his friendliness, his popularity as a lecturer, his wonderful
new compass.

"Is it not strange," Nicolo remarked to his father, "that although the great and learned, not only of Padua and Venice
but of many foreign places, revere my master Galileo, he has
never received recognition from Florence? Our city and the
entire state of Tuscany should be proud to claim him as a son."

The chamberlain agreed. He hastened to discuss the matter
with the wife of the grand duke, Fernando I. Grand Duchess
Christina was not without intellectual curiosity. She told her
chamberlain to suggest to Galileo Galilei that the court of the
grand duke was fascinated by accounts of his compass. Would
it be possible for the professor to spend his next holidays at
the ducal summer palace in the mountains? Here he might be
pleased to instruct the royal heir Cosimo in the manipulation
of the compass, which he had so successfully taught to so many
noble youths.

Galileo read and reread the invitation. He leaned back in his
armchair and shifted the cushions which propped his legs; for
this was one of the days that his arthritis tortured him cruelly.
But now he lost his pain in a very different ache that swelled
in his heart. After all these years he was still homesick for
Florence.

The rather stocky professor, his coarse red hair beginning
to recede from his temples, looked back through the years and
saw himself a wide-eyed little boy in his father's woolshop.
They had had so many good talks together there! His father
had spoken to him of Leonardo da Vinci, condemned for the
sin of pride to die far from Florence.

I am still young enough, thought Galileo, to have—by God's
grace—the best years of my life before me. I wish I might
spend them in Florence, my heart's home, serving the state as

faithfully as my ancestors did before me. Soldiers, statesmen, artists—an illustrious physician still remembered in Tuscany! If I win favor in the court I might be able to give our honored name to my little Vincenzio. And if he is recognized as my legitimate son, who knows how high he may rise in the service of the state, bringing new honors to the name of Galilei!

There were other reasons why Galileo longed to return to Florence. In spite of the honors heaped upon him in Padua, he believed he would hold a more distinguished position if attached to the Tuscan court. Like Tycho Brahe, court mathematician to Emperor Rudolph! thought Galileo. And if I might be free from lecturing and tutoring I could find more time for my own studies.

Hoping that the invitation from the grand duchess might prove a prelude to a permanent post in her court, Galileo eagerly accepted her invitation.

When summer brought him release from his duties at the university, the professor bade his friends good-by until autumn, and deposited with Marina a sum large enough to maintain the household during his absence. Galileo knew he would miss his children, especially his favorite little daughter Virginia. But he could not pretend to regret that it would be impossible to take Marina with him to the ducal summer palace. In Padua there was no criticism of their relationship. But in the Tuscan court she could be received only as his wife. He shrank from the thought of marriage to the woman whose beauty had dazzled him in the blue and gold Venetian days of his youth. The love that then had flamed so fiercely between them had burned itself out and now only gray ashes remained.

To Galileo's homesick eyes Florence seemed even lovelier than his remembered City of the Lilies. As soon as he could tear himself away from his admiring relatives—even his

brother-in-law, now that the dowry was paid, was friendly—
Galileo roamed along the twisted, narrow streets. He delighted
in all he saw: the cathedral into which he slipped for a moment's prayer; the Baptistery with its doors which Michelangelo
had called beautiful enough to be the gates of Paradise; the
tower of the Palazzo Vecchio surmounted by the iron lion,
flaunting its lily against the summer sky. He wandered to the
monastery of San Marco where Fra Angelico's frescoes still
moved him with their air of childish innocence. He paused
before the cell where the Dominican Savonarola a century before
had prayed and meditated before leaving his shadowy sanctuary
to defy prince and pope, until the hands of the public execu-
tioner silenced his rebellious preaching.

He sinned against Florence and against God, mused Galileo,
yet should he have been punished so terribly for proclaiming
what he believed was the truth?

Later, as Galileo stood on the Ponte Vecchio, spanning the
Arno, he again thought of the rebel friar; for no accountable
reason, he thought also of Giordano Bruno.

Galileo had never met the older scholar. But he had pondered long and earnestly over his writings, marveling how far
and fearlessly the unfrocked Dominican had wandered in his
defense of Copernicus. For Bruno, one of the greatest Italian
philosophers of the later sixteenth century, did more than argue
that the earth was a mere planet revolving around the sun. He
believed that many stars might be the centers of other groups
of worlds. If this be true, decided Giordano Bruno, could not
these distant worlds be also inhabited? And if the Saviour of
this earth died to save sinners, did it not follow that on the
most distant celestial body He must repeat the divine mystery
of His life and death?

Standing on the bridge above the Arno, brooding in the long

summer twilight, Galileo shuddered to recall his own defiance of the rector of the University of Pisa. Perhaps the old man had been right to denounce so vigorously anyone who sought new and forbidden paths. Bruno had accepted the teachings of the pious churchman Copernicus, only to find himself a rebel against the Church, a fugitive in many lands from the power of the Inquisition. What were his thoughts, wondered Galileo, when for eight years he suffered in a Roman dungeon, never seeing the light of day until he was led forth to be burned alive for his heresy?

Galileo crossed himself and, although he knew that Bruno deserved his sufferings in this world and the next, prayed that in God's own time the erring one might know his sins forgiven. "How dearly must a man love truth to give his body to the flames for her sweet sake?" Galileo asked himself. "Would I show such courage if threatened with torture and death?"

It was dark when he returned to his mother's house. Giulia Galilei, who had spent all day preparing a supper worthy of her distinguished son, scolded him shrilly for his tardiness. She declared that the kid, which she had purchased at a ruinous price, had roasted to the dryness of shoe leather; for the last hour she had been so worried lest harm had come to her darling that she had neglected the sauce, now quite unfit to serve to one honored by the friendship of the grand duchess. To please the flustered dame Galileo begged her to heap his plate. Between mouthfuls he praised the roast kid, the *pasta*, even the sauce which was indeed slightly scorched. But he was quite unconscious of what he ate. When his mother complained of the rising price of olive oil, the neglect shown her by the distant Michelagnolo and the disrespect of her daughters, he answered her so absently that she began to clear the table with a furious banging of dishes.

"With all your fine friends in Padua and those you expect to meet in the duke's summer palace, you are too high and mighty to listen to your old mother," she reproached him.

Galileo apologized. He wondered what she would say if he told her he was still puzzzling over the fate of Giordano Bruno, and how far a man might venture in his search for truth.

The remainder of Galileo's holiday passed pleasantly enough in the grand duke's mountain palace. The clear pure air and quiet unhurried life seemed to benefit the professor; he rejoiced to remain unplagued even for a short while by his old enemy, arthritis.

In Crown Prince Cosimo, still in his teens, Galileo found a charming and attentive, if not brilliant, pupil. The boy had not yet mastered the use of the new compass when the time arrived for Galileo to return to Padua. It was understood that the mathematician would soon pay another visit to court and renew his instructions.

"When I am a grown man and rule over Tuscany," promised Cosimo, "I will appoint you my court mathematician."

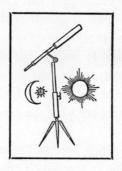

A TELESCOPE CANNOT LIE

GIFTS FROM THE grand duke—but no offer of a permanent post—came to Galileo. He made several more visits to Florence, where he was graciously received by his royal patrons. Court officials hinted that when Duke Fernando, now busily engaged in negotiating a marriage for Cosimo, had more leisure, he would no longer permit such a distinguished scholar to remain a mere professor in Padua. Galileo smiled his thanks, but shrewdly decided not to press for an appointment. If he did not seem too anxious to return to Florence he might expect a more advantageous offer.

For a little while Galileo had no time to be homesick for his beloved city. His domestic affairs absorbed him completely. After all the humdrum years with Marina Gamba, the household which he had maintained for her and the three children seethed with uncertainty. Marina was not too happy over Galileo's visits to the Tuscan court, his rich and noble friends, his appointments to distinguished academic societies in Florence and Padua.

Coming to Padua, she had felt herself secure as the mistress of the household of a young professor burdened with debt and not too sure of his position in university circles. Although without book learning, she surmised how famous Galileo had grown. She was shrewd enough to realize that while he mounted the ladder of worldly success, every year thrust her further into the background. Marina knew that since Galileo no longer loved her, he would never offer her what she now craved—the security of marriage.

I am used to my position here in Padua. But he could never present me as his wife at the duke's court, she decided. And now that I am growing old and losing my beauty, what will I do if he deserts me?

In her anxiety for a secure future, Marina was glad to listen to the urging of Giovanni Bartluzzi, a Venetian of her own age, who proposed marriage.

"But what will happen to our children?" demanded Galileo, when Marina informed him of her plans.

"We can send Virginia and Livia to a convent boarding school," suggested Marina. "In a few years they will be old enough for marriage; or if they have a vocation they can take the veil."

"And little Vincenzio?"

"While he still needs a mother's care, he must stay with me in Venice. His foster father has promised to treat him kindly. And he will be allowed to visit you—whenever you have time for him. Of course," she added hastily, "you will send me money regularly for his support."

"Of course!" agreed Galileo. He spoke cheerfully, but his heart was heavy at the thought of parting from the son in whom he took such pride. Yet he could not help feeling relieved. Vincenzio's keep and payment for the daughters' living and tuition in a convent would fall far below the extravagant sums Marina had always needed to maintain her household. Perhaps now he might be able to pay the last of his debts and even save a little.

With Vincenzio living with his mother and stepfather in Venice, and the two pretty daughters safely established in the Convent of San Matteo near Florence, Galileo turned back eagerly to his studies. He was about to settle down to the twin joys of a professor's life, research and instruction, when in the year 1609 he heard a traveler, just returned from the Low Countries, tell an amazing tale.

Some months before, Jan Lippershey, an optician of Middelburg, witnessed an accident which for centuries to come was to link his name with the greatest astronomical discoveries. Intent on the spectacle lens he was grinding, Lippershey was startled to hear a shout of laughter followed by an incredulous whistle. The disturbance came from his half-grown apprentice who sat on the high oaken window seat.

"What's the matter?"

The lad stuttered in his excitement. "Master, I was just polishing these lenses as you bade me—"

"Is that any reason why you should start shrieking like a heathen savage?" demanded Lippershey, frowning.

"But, Master, when I held up two at once to the light to make sure that they were as shining as you would have them, I saw—But you will never believe what I saw when I looked through them!"

"If you've mixed the lenses again, you lying knave, I'll give you the beating you deserve," shouted the short-tempered optician. He was about to return to his work when the boy, fearful but determined, approached the worktable.

"Please don't be angry. But I am willing to swear on the

Bible that when I looked out of the window just now I saw the belfry tower."

"Which any but a blind man could easily see!"

"Everything was upside down," the boy rushed on. "And I saw two great white storks standing over their nest near the chimney of the Town Hall."

"Have you been helping yourself to my bottle of schnapps, that you have the impudence to tell me such lies?"

The master reached for his cane. But the boy dodged the blow and ran back to the window.

"Just see for yourself how the glasses make everything close!" he pleaded. "If I lied to you, may I never kiss my sweetheart again."

"Drunk or lying," muttered Lippershey, reaching for the two lenses the boy held out to him. After a long, long look, the optician placed the lenses carefully down upon the window seat, then dropped them into the pocket of his work apron, and rubbed his startled eyes.

"If this is witchcraft," he muttered, "why should we both suffer from the same spell at the same moment? Not a word of this to anyone, do you hear? Go back to your work and try to be quiet while I puzzle over the matter."

When I held these two lenses a little distance apart and looked through them, pondered the maker of spectacles, they not only seemed to bring the buildings nearer, but they also magnified the storks which have always appeared like tiny white specks to my naked eye. Although the birds were upside down I could see them clearly. He took the lenses from his pocket and studied them. "One is concave, the other convex," he said. "Well, suppose I try two others, one concave, one convex, held at the same distance as before."

Again both master and apprentice took turns peering through

the lenses. Now equally excited, each pointed out to the other
a third stork, and even the much smaller weather vane on the
church tower. Then Lippershey gravely shook hands with the
goggle-eyed apprentice and not only granted him a half holiday
but gave him a bit of money that he might enjoy himself at a
neighboring tavern.

In a few hours Lippershey's experienced fingers had completed a tube with lenses at both ends. This he placed in the
window of his shop to attract passers-by. A few curious customers bought the "magic glass," which they considered as
merely a curious toy. But Count Maurice de Nassau, to whom
Lippershey presented one of his new instruments, exhibited it
to some of his military advisers. Could this spyglass, as he called
it, be so improved that it could be used to detect the movements of a distant enemy on the sea or on the battlefield?

"About ten months ago," Galileo later wrote in his controversial *Messenger of the Stars*, "a report reached my ears
that a Dutchman had constructed a telescope by the aid of
which visible objects, although at a great distance from the
eye of the observer, were seen directly, as if near; and some
proofs of its most wonderful performances were reported,
which some gave credence to, but others contradicted. . . .
I received confirmation of the report in a letter written
from Paris . . . which finally determined me to give myself up first to inquire into the principle of the telescope,
and then to consider the means by which I might compass
the invention of a similar instrument, which a little while
after I succeeded in doing, through deep study of the
theory of refraction; and I prepared a tube, at first of lead,
in the ends of which I fitted two glass lenses, both plane on
one side, but on the other side one spherically convex and

the other concave. Then bringing my eye to the concave lens I saw objects satisfactorily large and near, for they appeared one-third of the distance off and nine times larger than when they are seen by the natural eye alone. I shortly afterwards constructed another telescope with more nicety which magnified objects more than sixty times. At length by sparing neither labor nor expense, I succeeded in constructing for myself an instrument so superior that objects seen through it appear magnified nearly a thousand times, and more than thirty times nearer than if viewed by the natural power of sight alone."

By adding a third lens, Galileo made it possible to see objects, not upside down, but in their correct position. With his fourth telescope he was able to look upward. By the time he had completed his fifth instrument, crowds began to stand for hours before his house. Noblemen, students, peasants from the farms and professors from the university waited impatiently to peer through the wonder-working tube. Skeptics whose ears had refused to believe the reports could not deny the miracle their own eyes verified.

The telescope could not lie.

In a letter to a friend during this period, Galileo writes in all humility: "I give infinite thanks to God who has been pleased to make me the first Observer of Marvelous Things."

But the triumphant inventor could not resist boasting to the brother-in-law who had once hounded him in the matter of the unpaid dowry:

"As the news had reached Venice I had made such an instrument, six days ago I was summoned before their Highnesses, the *Signoria* and exhibited it to them, to the astonishment of the whole Senate. Some of the nobles and senators, although of a great age, mounted more than once to the top of the highest church tower in order to see sails and shipping that were so far off that it was two hours before they were seen, without my spyglass, steering full into the harbor. . . . Perceiving of what great utility such an instrument would prove in military and naval operations, and seeing that his Serenity the Doge desired to possess it, I resolved . . . to present it as a free gift. . . . I was commanded to bide awhile in the hall of the Senate, whereunto the Procurator, Antonio Prioli, one of the heads of the University of Padua, came, and taking me by the hand, said that the Senate, knowing the way in which I had served it for seventeen years at Padua, and being sensible of my courtesy in making it a present of the spyglass had ordered my election (with my good will) to the Professorship for life, with a salary of one thousand florins yearly; and as there remained yet a year to terminate the period of my last re-election in Florence, they willed that the increase of salary should date from that very day."

Galileo smiled as he pictured his mother listening to the great news. He could hear her exclaim: "Ah, if your poor father had only lived to see this day!" Poor soul, so lonely and unloved! Now he could cheer her a little with a really rich present.

He had no intention of allowing his telescope to remain an instrument useful only in warfare. When he had first heard of Lippershey's wonderful "toy" the inventor in Galileo had responded to the challenge. Could he reproduce—no, improve—the mechanism he had never seen? As he ground his own lenses, trying now this arrangement, now that, the scientist began to ask himself: "Instead of trying to bring within the range of the natural eyes those distant ships, suppose I had turned my telescope upon the heavens!" And he began to consider how his latest and strongest glass might be used to broaden the scope of astronomy.

Whenever the midnight heavens were clear, Galileo studied the stars. At first what he saw staggered him in its expansive grandeur. Hurrying to his study, he forced himself to write calmly of the revelation of the Milky Way he had just witnessed: "The Galaxy is nothing else but a mass of innumerable stars planted together in clusters. Upon whatever part of it you direct your telescope, straightway a vast crowd of stars presents itself to view; many of them are tolerably large and extremely bright, but the number of small ones is quite beyond determination."

Later he wrote: "I had determined to depict the entire constellation of Orion, but I was overwhelmed by the vast quantity of stars and by want of time."

He flung his quill pen and paper aside; for a long time he sat at the littered table, staring before him, his chin propped in his hands.

Would he live long enough, he questioned feverishly, to record even a fraction of the infinite wonders of the firmament? He recalled the hours he had squandered at concert and feast. Now he put aside his lute and music folios; whenever possible he refused himself to visitors; at times he became so preoccupied that even his lectures became a burden; he begrudged the moments he was forced to spend on his hasty, solitary meals.

Trembling with excitement, half afraid to be the first of all mankind to see the wonders he anticipated, Galileo climbed the stairs to his observatory. As though to bless this great adventure the full moon shone down upon him. Galileo remembered the myth he had read in Ovid, how Actaeon had been punished with death for daring to look upon the naked beauty of Diana, goddess of the moon. For a moment he hesitated to gaze on that which, since the beginning of time, had never been beheld by mortal eye. Then, throwing back his red mane defiantly, he turned his eyes upward.

The astronomer never knew how long he stood there, lost in amazement. When a servingman crept up with a cloak to protect his arthritic master from the night dampness, Galileo for once spoke so harshly that the fellow rushed away in terror. At last Galileo entered his study to record what he had just seen:

"I feel sure that the surface of the Moon is not perfectly smooth, free from inequalities and exactly spherical as a large school of philosophers considers with regard to the Moon and the other heavenly bodies. But that, on the contrary, it is full of hollows and protuberances, just like the surface of the Earth itself, which is varied by lofty mountains and deep valleys."

Again and again he studied the mountains of the moon, computing their height so accurately that no astronomer—even with the most powerful modern telescope—has ever been able to dispute the figures Galileo set down.

In the following January, 1610, Galileo made another stupendous discovery. When he turned his telescope upon Jupiter he observed two stars, small but very bright, to the east of the planet, and one to the west. On the following evening he was astonished to observe that all three stars were on the western side.

He began to wonder, runs his record, "how Jupiter could one day be found to the east of all the aforesaid fixed stars, when the day before it had been west of two of them; and forthwith I became afraid lest the planet might have moved differently from the calculations of astronomers and so had passed those stars by its own proper motion. I therefore waited for the next night with the most intense longing, but I was disappointed of my hope, for the sky was covered with clouds in every direction."

But the following night was clear and the astronomer was convinced that the "interchange of position belonged not to Jupiter but to the stars." Three nights after this discovery, Galileo saw a fourth of these moving stars. He lowered his telescope and staggered into his study so overwrought that at first he was unable to set down his epoch-making observation.

"Not stars but moons!" His excitement almost choked him. He flung open a window and leaned far out to fill his lungs with the night air. Above him the stars, whose secrets he was mad to probe, sparkled like tiny lamps. It had grown so late that not a single taper glowed in the neighboring houses. "Not stars but moons!" Galileo announced again to sleeping Padua, "and they revolve around Jupiter as the moon revolves around the earth."

It was thrilling enough to discover these satellites. But now Galileo's mind with one inductive leap brought his amazing observation to the conclusion he most desired to reach: he had made a tremendous step toward proving the theories of Copernicus.

"The moon revolves around the earth; the four moons of Jupiter revolve around the planet; the earth, Jupiter and the other planets revolve around the sun." Galileo looked up from the notes he had scrawled so hastily in his frenzy that the next day he was vexed to find them difficult to decipher. "Even a child, if he be as clever as my Vincenzio, will understand." He smiled wryly. "And since a telescope does not lie, even the Aristotelians will have to accept my discovery."

He told the story of these discoveries in his disturbing book, *The Messenger of the Stars*. Many astronomers who had long inclined to the theories of Copernicus greeted the volume with joy and gratitude. Wachenfels, as soon as he heard of the discovery of the moons of Jupiter, took a coach and hurried to see Kepler. He rushed into his friend's house and even before he removed his traveling cloak began to tell the astonishing story. Kepler in a letter to Galileo writes: "Such a fit of wonder seized me at a report which seemed to be so very absurd, and I was thrown into such agitation at seeing an old disputation between us decided in this way that between his joy and the laughter of us both, confounded as we were by such a novelty, we were hardly capable, he of speaking or I of listening. I long for a telescope." Later he manufactured a somewhat similar instrument of his own. Not only astronomers became excited over the telescope which had shown such marvelous things. The Venetian ambassadors and seafaring merchants carried to every corner of Europe the news of Galileo's triumph before the senate. In faraway kingdoms royalty demanded replicas of the new toy. In Austria Emperor Rudolph declared petulantly that a cardinal representing the papal court selfishly refused the telescope even when His Majesty wanted to look through it. In France, Maria de Medici, the stately dowager queen, shocked one of the most correct of court circles by stretching flat on her back in public that she might better enjoy the new pastime of studying the stars.

The Elector of Cologne complained that *The Messenger of the Stars* was incomplete since it contained no exact directions for constructing the new instrument. He suggested that Galileo share his secret with him and promised to repay him generously. By this time Galileo had learned from his disappointing experiences at the court of Tuscany not to put too much faith in princes. Even his incredible patience with the members of his demanding family wore thin when he received a long letter from Michelagnolo.

For once the musical parasite did not beg for money, although rumors of the wide sale of the telescope and the rich gifts Galileo received on its presentation must have tempted him. Instead, Michelagnolo urged his brother to gratify the elector's wish. He hoped, he wrote, that the elector would show his gratitude by granting promotion to the astronomer's humble relative! To make this promotion certain, Galileo should obtain letters of recommendation from the Grand Duke of Florence "to my master, but mind you, let them be good ones, such as you know how to get easily enough." For himself Michelagnolo desired nothing further except some lute strings—and a telescope. "If I am not a prince able to remunerate you, at any rate I am your brother," he reminded Galileo reproachfully.

Galileo was greatly heartened by a letter from Johannes Kepler. He wrote, after carefully considering all his fellow astronomer's claims, that if the Paduan professor were right, which Kepler was inclined to believe, his own book on cosmography had been proved entirely wrong. Such generous acknowledgment from such an authority warmed Galileo's heart and helped him to bear more patiently the criticism that was heaped upon him.

For, along with the increasing fame of the telescope, there arose such a storm of derision and abuse that a less courageous scientist than Galileo would have been tempted to announce that he had been in error.

"But Aristotle said . . .!" cried the scholars.

"Aristotle was always trying to discover new facts. He would have changed his opinions if he had been privileged to look through my telescope," Galileo retorted.

"Thomas Aquinas, the Angelic Doctor taught . . .!" thundered the churchmen. "How dare you deny what the Church has declared to be the truth?"

"I am a faithful child of the Church," Galileo defended himself. To those who accused him of impiety, he liked to repeat the words of Cardinal Baronius: "The Holy Spirit intended to teach us in the Bible how to go to Heaven not how the heavens go."

But many of the arguments against his book he tossed aside with scornful laughter. He had always had scant respect for numerology. Now he was reminded that there could be only seven planets, the sun and moon being included among these "wandering stars." Seven from time immemorial had been held a "sacred number"; how dared anyone add four moons and bring the counting up to eleven?

In Florence, a nobleman Francesco Sizzi, whose name survives merely because of his attacks on Galileo, solemnly stated:

"There are seven windows given to animals in the domicile of the head: two nostrils, two eyes, two ears, and a mouth. So in the heavens there are two favorable stars, two unpropitious, two luminaries, and Mercury undecided and indifferent. From this and many other similarities in Nature, which it were tedious to enumerate, we gather that the number of planets must necessarily be seven. . . . Moreover, these satellites of Jupiter are invisible to the naked eye and therefore can exercise no influence on the

Earth, and therefore would be useless, and therefore do not exist."

It was this same Francesco Sizzi who refused to look through the telescope in Galileo's observatory; perhaps he feared that he might really see the disputed satellites of Jupiter. Libri, an Italian philosopher of some reputation, also refused to look and be convinced. When he died shortly after, Galileo remarked that he hoped Libri would be permitted to gaze at Jupiter's moons on his way to heaven. Such frivolity added to the stories Galileo's enemies told of his shocking disrespect for sacred things.

In spite of his hasty temper, Galileo tried to maintain the calm and dignity sadly lacking in his opponents. At times he even grew humorous over the subject which had become the mainspring of his life. In 1610 he wrote to Johannes Kepler: "Why are you not here? What shouts of laughter we should have at this glorious folly, and to hear . . . arguments as if they were magical incantations and could charm the new moons out of the sky!"

During all this controversy Galileo continued his searchings of the heavens. One night he was amazed to observe the planet Saturn without what he had formerly thought were its attendant stars. "Have they suddenly fled?" he writes. "Was the appearance, indeed, fraud and delusion, with which the glasses have for so long mocked me and many others who have observed with me?" Five years later he was to describe these baffling attendant bodies as "handles." But because of the limits of his instrument, Galileo was never able to solve the mystery of the rings of Saturn.

News of Galileo's increasing fame reminded the grand duke that the astronomer, without actually petitioning for a position in the Tuscan court, had more than once expressed his desire to return to Florence. When Duke Fernando fell ill, Duchess Christina showed her confidence in Galileo by requesting him to draw up her ailing husband's horoscope. Such a task was distasteful to the scientist, who had long scorned astrology, but he was too diplomatic to refuse. Galileo, seldom at fault in his computations, now showed himself in error. Although he assured the lady that the stars foretold speedy recovery for the royal patient, Duke Fernando died shortly afterward.

Young Prince Cosimo, long Galileo's admiring pupil, had become ruler of Tuscany. Although he seemed to have forgotten his boyish promise to make the Paduan professor court mathematician, he continued to shower Galileo with favors. Cosimo sent him many rich gifts; there were invitations to visit the Tuscan court. Now, when Galileo named the four newly discovered satellites of Jupiter the "Medicean stars" in honor of the Duke's family, Vinta, the prime minister, offered him a post in his native state.

Galileo was to receive several titles and was expected to serve in two capacities. As first mathematician of the University of Pisa, he would have only nominal duty. But how pleasant it would be to hold a position of honor at an institution where he had once been neglected and despised! As philosopher and mathematician to the Grand Duke of Tuscany, he would be expected to act as arbitrator in scientific disputes. But his chief duty, Vinta wrote, would be to pursue his scientific investigations "and by them effect glory on his patrons and bring new benefits to the state."

"At last my salary will take care of my many family obligations," Galileo rejoiced to his friends. "And neither post will require the heavy labors that are undermining my health. I shall not have to live at Pisa or even give any regular lectures there.

Think of all the time I shall be allowed to spend in my observatory!"

One of the professors whom Galileo had invited to his house to celebrate the good news shook his head doubtfully.

"So you hope to continue your observations—and writing?"

"Of course! I shall have plenty of time to work on my inventions and books on mechanics and the constitution of the universe."

"Friend Galileo, like many other scholars, realize that yours is the greatest intellect of our time. But in many ways you have the trusting simplicity of a little child. You yourself know of the outcry certain great ones in the Church have made against your first book of discoveries. In Padua for eighteen years you have enjoyed perfect freedom. Surely I need not remind you that our rulers in Venice, so jealous of Rome's authority, if need be would shield you even from the power of the Inquisition."

"But in Florence I shall be under the personal protection of the Grand Duke of Tuscany," protested Galileo.

"Tuscany, as we all know, is under the thumb of the Holy Father at Rome."

"But," cried Galileo, "as soon as possible I shall visit Rome to demonstrate the truths my telescope has disclosed. Then the Pope and the Sacred College will be my friends and I shall have no cause to fear the enmity of the Inquisition."

"But have you not been happy in Padua these eighteen years?" someone asked.

"I have spent the happiest years of my life here," Galileo answered. "Here I have known true freedom; I could never have succeeded without it. Yet I can never forget how my father pictured Leonardo da Vinci dying so far away from his native land. Gentlemen, you all love with the same love the place of your birth, be it a humble mountain village or Venice, Bride of the Adriatic. To me Florence is my first and dearest love and I must return to her."

There was a short silence. Then the oldest among them rose to his feet.

"We have warned you, Galileo Galilei," he said. "Now there is nothing more to say. Friends"—and he raised his goblet—"before we bid farewell to the one who has shed such undying glory on our university, let us drink to his continued success and happiness."

While the others drank the toast, Galileo was forced to turn away to hide his tears. He felt that he would never again gather such a group of faithful friends around his table.

SPRINGTIME IN ROME

G ALILEO RETURNED TO the city of his ancestors on a bright September morning in 1610. Florence had never seemed so beautiful to her devoted son. The very poplars seemed more graceful, the smiling skies bluer than at Padua. His eyes rested in deep contentment on the encircling hills, silvery with olive orchards; on the yellow roads with here a cart drawn by great white oxen, there a flock of sheep ambling toward the market.

Through the central arches of the Ponte Vecchio he could glimpse the towers of San Miniato above its girdle of stately cypresses. Smiling, he turned to watch the fishermen letting down their nets from the windows of their houses which leaned crazily above the Arno.

As he walked slowly toward his mother's house, he looked with loving recognition on cathedral and palace, on shop and cloister. Galileo paused again and again to delight in the sights and sounds he had known in his youth: the mule-drawn carts which crowded the narrow streets; the market place, bright with vegetables and shrill with the cries of vendors of eggs and cheese, of cooking pots and old clothes, of rabbits and singing birds in wicker cages. And when he heard a dice player cursing his luck or a tattered beggar entreating alms, Galileo could have embraced them for kinsmen since they spoke with the beloved accent of Tuscany.

For once his own family gave him little trouble. His sisters and brothers-in-law were friendly and almost embarrassingly respectful to the royal mathematician. Galileo's two daughters, as meek and quiet in their severe school uniforms as little nuns, seemed happy and contented when their father visited them at the convent of San Matteo. Marina sent encouraging reports of young Vincenzio. And at last Galileo remained undisturbed by his mother's outbursts. Why heed the railings of a half-mad senile woman nearing her grave?

Still he was glad that it was no longer necessary for him to live with her. Until his own home with adequate provision for an observatory was prepared for him, he enjoyed the peace and quiet of the luxurious homes of several friends in turn.

When he visited Pisa, Galileo felt no little satisfaction to be welcomed so heartily. Could he have once been the student forced to leave the university because of poverty, denied a scholarship for his radical opinions? Now he was the famous Dr. Galileo, one of the leading scientists in all Europe—and court mathematician and philosopher to the grand duke, Cosimo II.

"I wonder," Galileo asked himself, returning from an evening party given by Cosimo, at which the entire court had listened with seeming eagerness to his explanation of his latest discoveries—"I wonder how long these golden days will last. When I was a schoolboy I read of a general who was honored by a triumph in Rome." So to remind himself that all glory is transient, he appointed a slave to ride beside him in his chariot and whisper at intervals: "Master, you are only human!"

But soon Galileo realized that he still had enough enemies in the Tuscan court to keep him from becoming too vainglorious. His old enemy the grand duke's uncle had never forgotten the matter of his discredited dredging machine. Francesco Sizzi, as stupid as he was vindictive, continued like an angry wasp to buzz his protests. A much more formidable foe was Archbishop Marcimedici, heir not only to that powerful family's glory but to more than his share of the Medici shrewdness. There were other enemies: some scholar's jealous of the astronomer's fame, which they believed undeserved; some Jesuits equally jealous for the refutation of their learned order. Now, in an uneasy truce, all waited in sullen silence for a chance to strike.

On the other hand, Cardinal del Monte in return for a present of one of Galileo's telescopes sent him his gem-encircled picture, along with a sympathetic and friendly letter. Father Clavius, leading mathematician of the influential Jesuit Roman College, wrote Galileo that many of its professors admitted the existence of the satellites of Jupiter. Best of all, Johannes Kepler, whom Galileo had always admired so deeply, publicly stated that through the telescope he had seen the much-disputed "Medicean stars."

Established in his observatory, Galileo continued his astronomical observations. A month after his arrival in Florence he made one of his most significant discoveries when he detected the phases of the planet Venus. Still puzzled by this planet's waning and waxing light, now disclosed for the first time through the telescope, Galileo was struck by its resemblance to the moon.

Galileo did not dare to make public what he had not yet verified. But he was eager to inform his fellow scientist, Kepler.

immediately of this important discovery. Suppose, thought Galileo, somebody pried into my letter. I must write it in Latin, of course, since Kepler knows no Italian and I am ignorant of German. But any scholar who reads my description of the phases of Venus. . . .

I have it! A commonplace quotation from the poet Ovid we both studied in our school days. It will be simple for Kepler to work out my cryptogram. But no, puzzled Galileo, after setting down the quotation I still need two more letters. For how can I spell Cynthia without a Y? Yes, I will need thirty-five letters in all.

Childishly pleased with himself, Galileo wrote to Kepler:

Haec immatura, a me, jam frustra leguntur—oy,
(These things not yet ripe for disclosure are read as yet by me in vain.)

which Kepler juggled into:

Cynthiae figuras aemulatur Mater Amorum.
(The Mother of Love, Venus, imitates the phases of Cynthia, the Moon Goddess.)

At last Galileo was able to proclaim to the world: "Venus rivals the phases of the Moon; for Venus being now arrived at that part of her orbit in which she is between the Earth and the Sun, and with only a part of her enlightened surface turned toward us, the telescope shows her in a crescent form, like the Moon in a similar position."

To Galileo this discovery that Venus revolved around the sun and received her light from it was the final proof he needed that the sun, not the earth, was the center of our universe. Here was the very evidence which the Aristotelians had defied the astronomer to present. They had always maintained that if the planets moved around the sun, then Venus and Mars should wax and wane like the moon. Now with his telescope Galileo could actually see these changes in progress.

Never again in the turbulent years that stretched before him was he to know such triumph. Here was the final refutation of the errors of Ptolemy, the proof which Copernicus had never been able to find.

Galileo's description of the sun spots, which he was one of the first to study, proved even more sensational than his accounts of the phases of Venus. Aristotle had declared the sun perfect and without blemish. So his followers still believed this statement as implicitly as they believed that there were exactly seven planets in the sky. Now the telescope clearly disclosed these imperfections. What was much more important was Galileo's conclusion that the spots on the sun indicated that the sun rotated on its axis. For his telescope showed clearly that these spots were perceived from different angles.

Now Galileo felt that he must go to Rome to receive what he had so long desired—the approval of the Church. He felt that he had already successfully demonstrated the truth of the Copernican theories to many of the most respected scholars of the Roman College. Surely, Galileo decided, the time had come for him to take the advice of Father Clavius and personally present to the Pope and his cardinals what the telescope had disclosed. Such a demonstration would make further revelations safer not only for the Florentine astronomer but for scientists everywhere in Catholic Europe.

More than his desire to advance the search for truth urged Galileo Galilei to set out on this momentous journey. Catholic born and reared, he had always been a devout believer. He had never for a moment wished to follow the Dominican, Giordano Bruno, in his rebellion against the Church. Whenever it was suggested that Galileo's daring pronouncements hinted of disbelief in the scriptures, he was deeply wounded. To him science and theology were worlds apart.

Now the time had come, thought Galileo, to win the approval of his spiritual superiors and to establish himself firmly before all the world as a devoted Catholic.

So in less than a year after his arrival in Florence, when spring, like Proserpina of the old legend, danced across the hills, dropping flowers as she moved, Galileo set out for the Eternal City. He was now forty-seven; but even a middle-aged man, often crippled by arthritis, might take pride in his new velvet cloak and richly embroidered tunic. The astronomer was especially proud of his one ornament, a necklace of fine gold. The grand duke had sent it to him several years before, after Galileo had named Jupiter's satellites in honor of the Medicis. Galileo leaned back on the cushions of the coach Cosimo II had placed at his disposal. Across the years he saw himself as the ragged student, hungry and footsore, limping toward the gates of the Eternal City. Suddenly he wished that his father had lived long enough to share such unbelievable good fortune.

At last he was in Rome—Rome, the proudest city of the whole earth, more beautiful than Venice, more imposing even than Florence, Galileo had to confess in rueful honesty. His eyes widened with wonder over the prodigal panorama of churches and palaces, of monuments, of bridges and loudly murmuring fountains. Rome, where Cicero had once thundered in the Forum; Rome, the city of conquering generals, who from their triumphal chariots had looked down on the bowed heads of captives brought from proud Jerusalem and faraway Britain!

London, Paris, Cologne—what were they but mushroom cities compared to this ancient stronghold of emperor and pope?

Across the Tiber loomed the Castel Sant' Angelo; built as a mausoleum for Emperor Hadrian, the mighty pile of weathered stone now served as a fortress. Galileo like every other Italian citizen had heard frightful tales of prisoners confined in its dungeons, some quickly murdered in their cells, others to suffer until their misery or public execution brought them release. In spite of the hot spring sunshine, Galileo shivered as he thought of these wretches cut off from the blessed light of day, often forgotten by those who had cast them into the darkness.

In the Piazza of the Vatican, Galileo stood brooding for a space before the Egyptian obelisk. The monument stirred the astronomer's old interest in mechanics. It had been brought to Rome by the first Caesar. Galileo marveled at the engineering feat which twenty-five years before had moved this stone— weighing from two hundred to five hundred tons—to stand like a grim sentinel before St. Peter's Church.

Galileo had heard that when the shaft was lowered the workmen first attended confession and two Masses were celebrated. All of the great ones of Rome and many of the highborn from every part of Italy were present to kneel with the workmen in prayer.

The workers were indeed blessed, for they labored for the glory of God and His Church, mused Galileo. Even as I have in my own way labored to unfold the glory of His universe to His children.

He straightened his shoulders; his eyes shone with sudden pride. Ah, Claudius Ptolemy of Egypt, once you ruled over the minds of men and like this obelisk towered above all who would dispute you! But your reign is over. Soon the whole world will accept the teachings of Copernicus and Kepler, yes, and of

Galileo; soon you will be but a relic saved from the past like this obelisk which my nation ravaged from yours!

So Galileo ranted in his pride, never dreaming how the years would bring him shame and suffering in this very city.

But during his second visit to conquering Rome he tasted the triumph of a conqueror and found it sweet. He often asked himself could this be really he, the wool merchant's son, received by the most distinguished scholars and ambassadors, flattered and feted by cardinals and princes.

The Jesuit astronomers of the Roman College cordially welcomed him to their observatory with its carefully planned windows, vast reference library and extensive equipment. Extensive, but not complete! Eagerly the black-garbed priests reached for the telescope he had brought and marveled as they turned it upon the heavens. Some opened their notebooks to jot down what they had seen; hastily they turned back to listen as the visitor from Florence explained what they had just witnessed. Galileo visited the college again and again. Not every scholar who listened to his lectures was prepared to accept all of his ideas. But even when a scientific argument grew heated, no one showed the slightest discourtesy to the distinguished guest.

Cardinal Bellarmino, an outstanding Jesuit philosopher, attended a demonstration of the telescope at the college. He seemed sufficiently convinced to grant Galileo's request for a statement by experts on the disputed *Messenger of the Stars.* To Galileo's delight the committee which the cardinal appointed, with only one difference of opinion, agreed on the validity of the astronomer's ideas.

His visit to the pope, Paul V, was less significant. The pontiff granted him only a brief audience; he wisely decided to leave scientific subjects to less exalted, but more learned, members of the hierarchy. The mightiest ruler in the world and the greatest scientist of the century spent a few moments in exchanging compliments. Then Galileo bent his knees, stiff from his crippling malady, that he might receive the precious papal blessing.

But a number of cardinals had more time to discuss astronomical matters. Cardinal Barberini, one of the intellectual leaders of his group, promised his friendship and support. Other influential members of the papal court flattered the astronomer with their interest; many of them, influenced by Barberini's example, spoke in the warmest terms of the *Messenger*, especially if they had not taken the trouble to read it.

The ambassadors of foreign governments and Roman noblemen of the proudest lineage visited Galileo and begged the privilege of having him for their guest. Banquet followed banquet—a medley of feasting and music and merriment, often ending with a serious hour given over to questions on the new discoveries. Galileo, a fascinating lecturer, always charmed his listeners.

Of all these feasts the Florentine always remembered most vividly the banquet given in his honor by Duke Federigo Cesi. The ducal palace was a treasure house of antique statues and priceless tapestries; the covers of rare weave on the long tables were almost hidden beneath rare crystal and heaped-high platters of gold and silver. Tall bronze lamps shone upon the rich velvets and plumes of the gentlemen, on their ladies' white shoulders and elaborately dressed hair, gleaming with jewels. Among the crimson and purples and saffrons of velvet and satin appeared the sober cloaks of scientists and philosophers, with here and there the bright robes of cardinals, the dark habits of the Jesuits and the white cloaks of the Dominicans.

Course followed course, each more elaborate than the last. Galileo, always a valiant man at the trencher, greeted each new dish with enthusiasm and emptied his wineglass again and again. The smiles of Rome's most famous beauties, who leaned across the table toward him, were even more intoxicating than the wine. Galileo had never been known to ignore a charming lady, but he was glad to turn away even from these sirens when Duke Federigo asked him to demonstrate the wonders of the telescope.

Rising in his place at the head of the glittering table, the host smiled down at the guest of honor.

"We may seem lacking in courtesy if we ask you to weary yourself at this late hour," he told Galileo. "But to many of us this evening will not be complete unless you, the star of this bright company, point out for our pleasure the stars you have gathered under your scepter."

"Scepter? He must mean the telescope! Our dear duke has turned poet," a Titian-haired beauty from Venice giggled into Galileo's ear.

"Yes! We would look through the telescope." "The telescope!" cried several voices.

Galileo rose to his feet a little unsteadily. At that moment he felt himself the equal of any prince in all that proud company. I, Galileo Galilei am not unworthy of my ancestors, he exulted. They ranked among the mighty ones of Florence, but I have risen above them all. I am greater even than the Grand Duke of Tuscany. For I have become a king—with my telescope for a scepter.

"Have you brought your telescope?" asked Duke Federigo.

Galileo laughed.

"In my younger days," he said, "when I attended a feast— though nothing so splendid as this with which you have honored me—I always brought my lute. I always hoped that I might be asked to join the musicians, who played after supper was over."

He pretended to fumble beneath his cloak. The lady from Venice pouted a little.

"You brought only your lute? My uncle the doge has told me of the wonders your telescope performed for him, and I had hoped—"

"But who would join an earthly orchestra when he might direct the dance of the stars?" cried Galileo. "Fortunately tonight the heavens are clear and I will be able to show you sights you never dreamed of." He smiled down into her bold eyes. "My servant who waits for me in my litter guards my telescope," he told the duke, "so if you will bid each to wait patiently for his turn—"

The duke nodded approval; several pretty ladies clapped their hands. But a stern-faced professor from the Roman College muttered of the folly of degrading a scientific demonstration into an epilogue for an evening's gormandizing; while his neighbor, an aged cardinal, gathered his robes about him and begged his host's permission to retire.

"My physician has imposed early hours on me, and as it is already long past my bedtime—" he murmured. He decided that this was not the proper moment to declare that it was beneath the dignity of a prince of the Church to give credence to Galileo's mummery.

But nearly all of the merry company remained to follow their host and Galileo—proudly carrying his telescope—to the highest tower of the palace. On the stone-ringed balcony the astronomer felt the cool night wind clearing his head and steadying his nerves. Now he no longer swaggered and jested. As he adjusted the instrument he again became the teacher, explaining that tonight observers would be fortunate enough to see Jupiter and its four satellites, the "Medicean stars."

The duke was the first to look through the miraculous lenses;

he was properly impressed. Several guests followed and expressed their wonderment. Then the Venetian lady, taking her place, declared laughingly that if she actually saw what she had been promised she would reward the astronomer with a kiss. Now Galileo frowned at her jesting. One should approach the revelation, which still moved him so profoundly, in awe and silence!

The lady peered through the glass and announced that she could see the planet and its four attendant stars very clearly. Then: "Just another minute," she pleaded. "Let me lower it a little . . . then perchance I shall see—" She gave a shrill, triumphant laugh. "Yes, the Church of St. John. The cross—the loggias—the lighted lamp. By all the saints, under the lamp I can make out the inscription above the door!"

A skeptical astronomer, forgetting etiquette in his scientific zeal, rudely pushed her aside. He gazed long and earnestly, then turned to Galileo.

"Sir," he said humbly, "I must ask your forgiveness before this exalted company. For I have been foolish enough to believe your detractors, who claimed that you had painted on the lenses of your instruments what you predicted the observers should see. But our noble host," bowing toward the duke, "says he saw the satellites of Jupiter. And with the same glass I have just been able to read the inscription our Holy Father Pope Sixtus commanded to be engraved over the church door. May those who slandered you be confounded, for you have never practiced the trickery of which they accused you."

Galileo's heart warmed at this further demonstration of his scientific integrity. But his happiness died when he discovered that the majority of the duke's guests were far more interested in trying to read the inscription of Pope Sixtus than to see the moons of Jupiter.

I give them the stars—and they turn like so many children to play with colored balls! he thought in disgust. Galileo felt like a juggler at a fair surrounded by gaping yokels. He hoped that the Venetian beauty would forget her promise. In his new mood of abasement, the touch of her painted lips would surely be the last shame he needed to make the evening a painful memory. He was relieved when she tripped away, still laughing, ogling above her huge feathered fan the gallant who guided her down the stairs.

"I have passed my days of drunken compliments and kisses," Galileo muttered to himself after his servant had helped him to bed. "I am getting to be an old man who should avoid banquets; better I should spend my nights reading the heavens. For who knows when the darkness will come?"

His arthritis always troubled him less in the mild spring weather. But he had not heeded the warnings of the duke's own physician back at Florence. Too much hurrying about, too much excitement, far too much rich food and wine!

"I needed no physic when I was a lean, starving student at Pisa," he grumbled, as he painfully turned in his bed and reached toward the table for the medicine the Florentine doctor had prescribed for him. He mixed the draught, tasted it, made a wry face, sipped a little, then flung the glass upon the floor.

What fools even the most celebrated physicians are! I doubt whether my esteemed ancestor, Galileo Galilei himself, could have concocted a drug to take away my pains. Well, he philosophized as he blew out his candle, it may have been for the best that I did not continue my medical studies to please my disappointed father. Else now, like all the other asses of the profession, I would be unable to cure my own sickness and could only rail at myself for my stupidity.

A CLOUD IN THE HEAVENS

IN JUNE GALILEO returned to Florence confident that he had
successfully overcome any opposition the Church might have
held against his writings. He brought with him a special papal
blessing for the grand duke, who listened with much interest
to his court mathematician's account of the friendliness of the
powerful Roman College. He smiled approval when he read
the enthusiastic message of Cardinal del Monte: "Were we
living in ancient Rome, Galileo would have been certain of a
statue in his honor in the capital."

"You have brought much honor to Tuscany," said the grand
duke.

But Galileo's hunger for honor and fame had suddenly left
him. He was like a child who has been allowed to stuff himself
with sweetmeats and turns to more wholesome food. Now all
he wanted was to return to his work. His illness in Rome, although short, had been severe and had left him badly frightened. Suppose he grew so crippled that he could no longer rise

from his bed to observe the heavens? Suppose his rapier-keen brain should become faltering and senile along with his weakened body? There was so much work left for him to do and at best the span of a man's fruitful years was far too short to accomplish the tasks the scientist had set for himself. Galileo hastened to his desk to write down what he had learned and wished to teach to all mankind.

Tycho Brahe was fortunate, mused Galileo, as he arranged and rearranged his notes. For when he died he left his instruments and his writings to Kepler, the one scientist capable of interpreting them. But can I hope for such an heir?

Galileo did not turn immediately to the study he hoped to make his lifework—a complete vindication of the Copernican theory. His interest in mechanics was just as lively as it had been in his student days at Pisa. Then he had puzzled over the problem of specific gravity—the relation of the weight of any object to the amount of water it displaces—and had at last triumphantly produced his hydrolic scales.

Now he took up the subject again, in order to study its fundamental aspects further and to present a more comprehensive thesis on the problem.

In his essay he developed the ideas of Archimedes more fully and again contradicted the opinions of Aristotle. Galileo pointed out that ice floats on the top of a stream simply because it is lighter than water and not because of its shape, as the followers of Aristotle insisted. "This demonstrated," said Galileo, "that water is the great exception to the rule that cold contracts bodies, while heat expands them." He wrote also that even air has a definite weight. This statement shocked everybody who held the prevailing "common-sense" view.

The essay was an important step forward in the understand-

ing of both specific gravity and heat. Unfortunately for Galileo
it was considered a challenge to the Aristotelians, who were
still eager to carry on their old feud. The court mathematician
was promptly attacked by a vindictive anonymous pamphlet on
the subject, addressed to Galileo's bitter enemy the Archbishop
of Florence.

In collaboration with his former pupil Father Benedetto Castelli, now professor of mathematics at the University of Pisa,
Galileo wrote a long and too passionate reply. In it he appealed
for freedom of thought among scholars:

> "Be grateful to the man who relieves you of errors, and
> do not resent it as if you were roused from an agreeable
> dream," he warns. . . . "My opponents like to cling to the-
> ories of ancient times because they wish their ignorance to
> be common to all men, just as at the time of a pestilence
> death is less bitter than it seems in a world of healthy
> men. . . . I value more the discovery of a simple truth
> than a lengthy pondering of the loftiest questions without
> any concrete result."

The last not too tactful statement did little to soothe the feelings of certain scholars; they had spent their energy trying to
defend a dying system while Galileo brought forth truths to
support a new conception of the universe.

Then from Augsburg, Germany, came another attack which
roused the never-patient Galileo to new fury. About the time
Galileo had first announced his discovery of the sun spots
similar claims had come from reputable astronomers of England and Germany. But now an astronomer, who preferred to
be nameless, claimed the distinction of being the initial dis-

coverer; what angered Galileo most was that the unknown scientist gave an Aristotelian explanation of his discovery.

Galileo studied this report with painful care. To many it might have seemed a waste of breath to answer an anonymous attack; but Galileo could never resist a battle, when what he considered scientific truth was involved. In his essay he boldly declared his belief in the theories of Copernicus. This he enlarged to book length and arranged to have it published in Rome.

He knew now that there could be no more evasions. In spite of his late triumph in Rome, letters from friends close to the papacy warned him that his enemies were increasing, that he was actually being watched as a suspect by the dread Inquisition.

In Florence those who hated Galileo came out boldly against him, knowing that the grand duke, so subservient to the papacy, would not defend the court mathematician. At Santa Maria Novella, Father Caccini, whose ingenuity in puns seems to have surpassed his knowledge of science, preached to a large and interested congregation on a seldom cited text: "Ye men of Galilee, why stand ye gazing up into heaven?"

Many Florentine noblemen, thinking of their own advancement in court, grew cool or openly unfriendly. Vinta, the prime minister, long Galileo's supporter, died; Galileo's patron Grand Duke Cosimo II died also. He was succeeded by his son Fernando II, still a child, who was under the regency of his mother and grandmother. The latter, Dowager Grand Duchess Christina, had long felt kindly toward the astronomer. But she had championed him as a friend, not a scientist; she was now old and growing ineffectual. Galileo began to grow afraid.

But not for long! As ever, opposition forced him to battle

more recklessly. In Florence, in Pisa, especially in Rome, secular followers of Aristotle joined forces with churchmen hostile to Galileo's ideas. The scientist had been sure that in good season all but the most reactionary of the Aristotelians would be convinced. But he felt that for personal reasons this was the time to win over those who accused him of impiety. He must persuade them that a man might follow the trail Copernicus had blazed across the heavens, yet remain a faithful Catholic. How dare ignorant priests like Father Caccini, who very likely had never read a page dealing with the new cosmogony, denounce it as heresy?

Galileo was shocked to hear that in Rome the writings of Copernicus might be placed on the Index of books forbidden to pious Catholics. He began a long and impassioned letter to Cardinal Dini, hoping to gain his influence with the papacy's board of censors.

Pausing to construct a pungent sentence, Galileo's eyes, which now tired so easily, fell upon his lute. Although he rarely played it, he kept it on his desk as a remembrance of his little Virginia. How sweetly the child had sung to his music in Marina's pretty vine-covered house in Padua, Galileo reflected. And now my daughters—whom I find time to visit so seldom—have no home but their convent cell in Arcetre while I am lonely here. But who am I to be the guardian of two young girls? My mother with her mad rages would be even worse; my sisters would surely neglect them in their care for their own children. . . . He picked up the lute and gazed at it tenderly. Suddenly he flung it back upon the desk and triumphantly set down the figure his instrument had suggested:

"In undertaking to reconcile the texts of the scriptures with the new doctrine," Galileo wrote the cardinal, "it is necessary to have complete knowledge of these doctrines; for it is impossible to tune two strings while only listening to one."

But Galileo's protest, although answered courteously enough, seemed of little worth. The representatives of the Church continued to attack him and certain of his followers as heretics. Desperate, he resolved to carry the fight to Rome.

Now no Roman triumph waited for Galileo. Here were no banquets in his honor while the proudest dignitaries in the world's proudest city jostled one another to look through his fabulous telescope. Father Clavius, who had remained a true friend to Galileo, even while disagreeing with many of his ideas, had recently died in Rome. The faculty of the Roman College had grown less enthusiastic in their praise. Many former friends were cool in their greetings or tried to avoid the astronomer altogether.

Still Cardinal Bellarmino and several others high in the Pope's esteem received the visitor with every sign of cordiality. When Galileo protested against the suspicions of the Inquisition, these diplomats refused to discuss the matter, since its actions were carried on in greatest secrecy. But he was assured that the charges against him would not be carried further—if he, as teacher and writer, were willing to follow the dictum of the Church concerning Copernicus.

"And what is the latest word of Holy Church concerning Copernicus?" asked Galileo bluntly.

Patiently one of the august body repeated what the scientist so greatly feared: Pope Paul V, after the latest report of his experts, would shortly suspend the book that declared the sun stood at the center of the universe and that the earth revolved around the sun.

Galileo bowed his head, knowing that his visit to Rome had

been in vain. True, since there was no longer any threat of imprisonment by the dread Inquisition, he might return to his beloved Florence. But if the theories of Copernicus were now definitely under the ban, how dared anyone defy Rome by defending them? Galileo felt that he could never write or teach freely again.

On his return Galileo established himself in a beautiful villa he had purchased at Arcetre on one of the hills overlooking Florence. Here he found relaxation cultivating the flowers and fruit trees and rare shrubs in his garden. Often a new idea would strike him and he would drop his spade or pruning hook to return to his desk or workbench. He began but did not finish an instrument which magnified greatly small objects placed beneath its lenses.

Strange, he mused, how after reaching for the stars, I can find pleasure watching an ant scurrying under my glass! From the moon—to a tiny pebble! And someday some man much wiser than I may fathom great mysteries in both which I have never even dreamed of!

Here at Arcetre he had contrived an observatory tower to house his telescope and other instruments. It was impossible for him to cease from observing the heavens—even though he feared he would not dare to write another book on the "marvelous things" he might still discover there.

Now he was so near the Convent of San Matteo that when his health permitted he was able to walk along the dusty road to the low stone building which housed his two daughters. Galileo was rather relieved when he learned that the young girls both intended to take the veil. Virginia with her childlike sweetness and purity seemed to have a real vocation; her fond father could already picture her as a serenely happy Bride of

Christ. Livia, whose moods varied from sullen silence to violent rage, painfully reminding him of her erratic grandmother, might be happier, too, under convent discipline than out in the world, forced to face the problems of a wife and mother.

"But how long will I have to wait for grandchildren?" Galileo asked himself. "Not that my dear brother will suffer our name to die out," he comforted himself, thinking of the thriftless Michelagnolo's ever increasing family in Munich. "I am still burdened with paying for the education of my nephews and the dowries of my nieces, and it will soon be time to begin looking for a suitable wife for my own Vincenzio."

He sighed when he thought of Vincenzio who on every visit seemed to resemble his absent uncle more closely.

"The lad has all of Michelagnolo's charm and laziness," decided Galileo, who no longer could delude himself into thinking that the boy's precocious shrewdness indicated intelligence. "The same lack of brains and sense of responsibility, without my brother's talent as a musician. But perhaps he may change as he grows older," he tried to comfort himself.

Vincenzio often visited his father at Arcetre; he showed neither gratitude for Galileo's generosity nor respect for his prominence. At Marina's death the youth spent a short time at the villa before leaving for the University of Pisa. His going left the charming little house cold and lonely.

For several days Galileo avoided his desk, piled high with unanswered letters from distinguished correspondents; he shunned both observatory and workroom. Only his garden seemed to bring him comfort. As he rested under his favorite olive tree his memory pictured Marina, not as he had last seen her—cold, indifferent, willing to desert him for a new lover— but as the passionate, laughing girl of his Venetian honeymoon. Was it possible that he, the slow-moving dour scholar, had ever echoed her laughter and pleased her with his love songs? When the dampness drove him indoors he forced himself to go to his desk; here he sat, too heartsick to write a line or even to reach for his pen. He lifted his lute from beneath a pile of papers; but although he held it for a long time he did not sound a single note.

THE SHADOWS DEEPEN

BEFORE LONG THE quiet was shattered by the invasion of Michelagnolo, his wife, a brood of unruly children and the family servant. The youngest boy trampled down the choicest flowers in Galileo's garden; the oldest girl, mean eyed and inquisitive, was discovered prying among his precious manuscripts. The servant insisted on preparing foreign messes in the kitchen, raising bedlam until the housekeeper, after a losing battle, resigned her post. Galileo tried to adjust matters with Michelagnolo's stout, sleepy wife. But as the dame understood no Italian and Galileo knew no German, it seemed best to call in Michelagnolo to arbitrate. This was difficult as he spent practically all of his time in taverns, drinking and gossiping and bragging of his triumphs in the Munich Court. When his older brother finally managed to corner him the musician shrugged off all complaints, declaring that an artist could not be expected to trouble himself with household affairs.

Whenever possible Galileo sought refuge in the quiet and peace of the convent of San Matteo. He saw little of Sister Archangel, as Livia was called in her new life; after a formal greeting she seemed to prefer to busy herself with her own affairs. But as soon as Sister Maria Celeste, his first-born, obtained permission to spend an hour with her father she comforted him with her loving sympathy.

"Did your cruel pains keep you awake again last night?" she would ask, noting the heavy circles under his eyes. "Before you leave, I shall ask Sister Catherine for a draught to bring you sleep. You know she is our apothecary and very wise in all manner of drugs. Sometimes she allows me to help her gather and dry herbs and label the little packets. She says I am very skillful for my age and that soon she may recommend that I be made her assistant. And I will be given duties in the infirmary!" Her gentle eyes glowed with happiness. "It will be a blessed thing to be permitted the care of our aged and sick sisters," she murmured.

"I wish I had you to nurse me when I am ill," Galileo said.

Her tender face grew suddenly grave. "Indeed, Father, I often wish that the rules of our order allowed me to visit you. I do not want to go out into the world any more; it frightens me. But it would bring me great happiness to nurse you and to care for your house. I thank God every day for permitting me to be one of His servants. But I still regret that I must be parted from you."

Encouraged by his interest, Sister Maria Celeste, usually so silent and withdrawn, prattled like a child. She repeated the story of the foundress of the Poor Clares, established at Assisi over four centuries before.

"When St. Clare learned of the good deeds of St. Francis and his brothers in God, she retired from the world and surrounded herself with noble ladies, who were attracted by her holiness. Like St. Francis they all embraced poverty; they gave all their wealth to the poor, keeping no possessions but the convent which sheltered them, and supported themselves with the work of their own hands."

Galileo looked down at his daughter's which rested in the lap of her coarse gray robe. Once they had been pink tipped, as soft and white as her indolent mother's; now the nails were broken and the skin coarsened and discolored from labor in the garden and with the scrubbing pail.

"We still observe the vow of poverty St. Francis taught," the girl continued, "and, like his brothers, pledge ourselves to chastity and obedience. It is not hard to obey our Lady Abbess for she is very kind and patient with our faults. Sometimes she allows us to dispense with the obligation of silence. That brings great happiness to the younger nuns." She flashed one of her rare smiles. "They often find it hard to refrain from conversation until the recreation hour."

"But, daughter, you are still very young, and it must be hard to be silent so long. I remember what a lively chatterbox you used to be!"

Again she smiled. "I am too busy now. Our day is divided between work and prayer and I love both. When I first took the veil I was often very hungry. Even when I was on my knees"— and she blushed in shame—"I sometimes remembered the ortolans and rich hot meats we ate in Padua. Here we have no meat even on Christmas. And there are many fasts that we may learn to mortify ourselves."

"But, child," he protested, "you have never been overstrong, and with your constant labors, you require—"

The bell for evening prayer interrupted him.

"Father, I need nothing. For now I have learned to be satisfied with Christ, the Living Bread."

Galileo felt his throat tighten. "My daughter, I sorely need your prayers. Pray for me."

"I always do," she said and smiled into his eyes before she walked away softly in her woolen sandals toward the chapel.

When Galileo was unable to visit her, Sister Maria Celeste gained permission to write to him. Her little notes, usually accompanied with gifts from the convent garden or kitchen, were delivered to the villa by the dour old steward of San Matteo. In spite of her youth, the nun wrote like an indulgent mother fretting over her only son away at school.

How different from his own mother, thought Galileo now without bitterness. He tried to forget certain angry letters she had sent long ago to Pisa when he was lonely and discouraged. But the stormy, passionate woman now lay silent in her grave. And he was the last man to bear a grudge against the dead.

Was he confined to his bed again? Maria Celeste would ask. Perhaps he might profit from a drink of steaming tea brewed from the herbs enclosed in her letter. Dear Sister Catherine recommended them; she also prayed for his speedy recovery to health. . . . Galileo pictured the two nuns—Sister Catherine, bent and withered, and his own little Maria Celeste—praying together; he felt strangely comforted.

Many of the gentle nun's letters to her father have been saved. But not one of Galileo's notes to Maria Celeste has been discovered. Yet he must have written her regularly for she comments: "I put by carefully the letters you write me daily, and when not engaged in my duties I read them over and over again."

During one of Galileo's illnesses the steward brought biscuits which the young nun had baked in a mold of curious design. Another gift to tempt the invalid's uncertain appetite was a small basket containing four late autumnal plums, which, wrote Maria Celeste, "I have succeeded in procuring. . . . If they are not in as great perfection as I could have wished, you will take the will for the deed." The next day she prepared a custard for her father.

Although her prescribed duties kept her busy, she seemed to welcome added tasks for her father's sake. Does he like baked pears and quinces? asks one note. In another she inquires whether his linen collars require washing or mending. Evidently several of her sister nuns aided in her love labors, for she tells Galileo: "I send back the rest of your shirts which we have been working at." Then, warning her father, who knew more of mathematics than needlework: "I cannot begin working at the dinner napkins till you send the pieces to add on. Please bear in mind that the said pieces must be long, owing to the dinner napkins being a trifle short."

Her teeth often gave her great pain; her health, always delicate, was taxed by the strict rules of her order. Yet she never complained of the sparse, monotonous fare, or the discomforts of her cell, hot in summer and cold in winter. "Doubtless," so she dismisses her weakness and suffering, "our Heavenly Father would give me health, too, if it were good for me."

In his turn Galileo delighted in sending frequent gifts to the convent. Not for his frail daughter, since a nun dedicated to poverty has no use for worldly baubles. Although she seems to have been pleased with a much-needed coverlet for her hard pallet. There is no record that she ever asked anything for herself but a plain little breviary when her own prayer book began to fall apart from constant use.

Sister Maria Celeste writes her father that the food and wine which he sent to the Mother Superior of San Matteo was disposed of as the directress deemed best. The plump partridge and cream cheese will be enjoyed by the invalids in the infirmary. The Mother Abbess, she adds, is truly grateful for the gift of thread and flax so sorely needed in the sewing room. The seeds will be planted at once in the garden. And it would help if Galileo sent something to relieve the wants of the hungry poor who come so often to beg at the convent's gates.

It seems unlikely that during her few hours of recreation Maria Celeste ever read a line of her father's scientific writing. But, secluded and ignorant as she was, she had heard much of his fame. She was delighted when he showed her praise-filled letters from the leading scientists of Europe. She rejoiced when his health permitted him to continue his work which she realized was his only happiness.

But Galileo's writing grew more difficult. He had thought it would be easy to work if Michelagnolo's undisciplined brood no longer swarmed through his villa and garden. Although he hated to quarrel with his brother, Galileo was secretly relieved when the musician threatened to leave Arcetre and upbraided him for his stinginess. This after all Galileo's past favors, months of hospitality and his aid in securing a stipend for Michelagnolo's eldest son to study music in Rome! Always restless, Michelagnolo bade his wife and the quarreling servant to pack their possessions that the family might return to Munich.

Now Galileo, when his health permitted, spent long, undisturbed hours at his desk. But for the first time in his life he found it almost impossible to set down a single word on paper. Even when he wrote on nonscientific matters to his many correspondents, he felt that someone was looking over his shoulder. He trusted his adoring servants; he tried to be discreet in all he wrote. But he knew that the Inquisition had a thousand eyes. His most innocent statement might be misquoted since he could never free himself from the charge of "intimacy with suspected persons" guilty of the crime of accepting Copernicus. Yet he felt that he would rather die than break off communication with such dear and respected disciples as Castelli.

But it seemed that the heavens themselves blazed forth a command that Galileo should again write of their wonders.

Three comets appeared to stir the imagination of astronomers, while the ignorant folk fearfully wondered what calamities were heralded by the fiery visitors. This was the year 1618 when the Thirty Years' War began, bringing the horrors of death, pestilence and famine. It was to destroy great cities and lay waste the countryside, reducing by a third the population of Germany.

Galileo had been too ill to study the blazing phenomenon. It happened that Prince Leopold of Austria journeyed to Italy at this time. Like all distinguished visitors to Florence, he was curious to meet Galileo. From his sickbed the astronomer told Leopold his own theory of the nature of comets, on which he longed to do further research. A little later Galileo was outraged when he heard of a public lecture on the subject given by Father Grassi. The Jesuit scientist, although he had included in his address the latest discoveries in astronomy, had neglected even to mention Galileo's name.

Galileo was imprudent enough to show his resentment at the omission. When one of his disciples brought him an essay he had written against Grassi, the old lion felt his strength returning. He rose from his bed to edit what the younger scholar had written in his master's defense, then permitted the joint work to be published.

In reply Father Grassi wrote a thesis which was a violent personal attack on Galileo. In it the priest listed the royal mathematician's discoveries—attributing every one of them to other scientists. Along with these slanders Grassi managed to insert a malicious and most dangerous question: "Galileo's pupil," he wrote, "had not even mentioned the Copernican theory in his essay. Was it possible that Galileo no longer believed in the theory which the Church had recently condemned?"

"Dare I reply to Grassi's lies?" Galileo asked his most trusted friends. "It will be simple enough to clear myself of his charges that I have robbed other scholars of their rightful fame to build up my own. But what can I answer concerning my views on Copernicus? Since my visit to Rome I have been most discreet; I have not set down in writing a single word on the subject. But if now I claimed disbelief in Copernicus—which I shall never do—my denial would only give more prominence to his question. And if I ignore this charge altogether, it will be construed as an admission of guilt."

Those he consulted were divided in their counsel. But on one point they all agreed. The War of Religion, as the Thirty Years' War was called, made it more dangerous than ever for a citizen of the Catholic state of Tuscany to oppose the opinions held in Rome. The slaughter on the battlefield was the bloody climax of the struggle which had begun with Luther's Reformation. In its efforts to crush the rising power of the Protestants, the Church had endeavored to root out evil and rebellion through its Counter Reformation, thus striking at heresy from within as well as without the fold.

Luther had dismissed the ideas of Copernicus by calling him a fool and accusing the canon of impiety. So no one could label his theory as Protestant. But Galileo knew that in these days of intensified religious hatred he would sign his death warrant by defying Rome. For the Inquisition would feel forced to punish an avowed Catholic who had won such fame that he would be capable of leading many true believers into error.

He knew also that he could hope for no support from his royal patrons since now the Jesuits actually controlled Tuscany.

But in Rome his old pupil and admirer Monsignor Ciampoli, now the Pope's secretary, had great influence in the Vatican itself. He and a few prominent churchmen who still remained faithful urged Galileo to vindicate himself and promised their support.

Three years after Father Grassi's libel Galileo published his answer. He was cautious enough to avoid reopening the bitter controversy over Copernicus. Neither denying nor reaffirming his belief in the condemned system, Galileo declared he still believed he might be able to demonstrate a new cosmology. He submitted the manuscript to the all-powerful board of censors in Rome. Here certain Jesuits fought its publication. But the influence of Galileo's friends within the Church—and the book's disarming tone—won against all prejudice, and permission was at last secured for its publication.

When *Sagiattore* was published Galileo was almost sixty. His long tormenting illness and his ever-mounting fear of his enemies had combined to make him a tired old man. But now when every day brought more flattering comments on his book, his youthful vigor seemed to return to him. He wanted to throw his cap into the air and shout like his rakish student son Vincenzio at the latest news from Rome. For Galileo's old friend and protector, a lover of the arts and sciences, had just been elevated to the papal throne. Cardinal Maffeo Barberini, as the pope, Urban VIII, now ruled the Catholic world. He had once written verses in praise of Galileo's discoveries and had signed his letters to the scientist, "your affectionate brother."

Galileo's hopes were unjustified. As a young cardinal, Barberini had found no difficulty in reconciling the new science with the old faith; he had not hesitated to encourage freedom of thought. Even after his elevation, Pope Urban was reported to have said of the Church's suppression of Copernicus' writings: "This has never been our intention, and if it had been in our hands this decree would never have been promulgated." But the triple crown had been placed upon Urban's head in an era of increasing intolerance and fanaticism. The rebellion of Luther and Calvin which the Catholics now challenged on many a bloody battlefield forced the new pontiff to forsake his former liberalism.

But for the moment Galileo was greatly encouraged by Pope Urban's friendliness. When in the spring of 1624 the astronomer journeyed to Rome to offer his congratulations, the Pope granted him a number of private audiences. Urban promised the gratified father a stipend for the further education of Vincenzio. He bestowed on his old friend a painting in a gold frame, a silver medal and a collection of small sacred pictures which His Holiness had blessed.

If Grassi and his followers were displeased, they growled in secret; the friends of Galileo and freedom of thought openly rejoiced. They were no longer fearful of Galileo's future when they learned that Pope Urban had written a long letter to the Grand Duke of Tuscany, warmly praising his court mathematician.

In writing to the youthful grand duke, Ferdinand II, the Pope said: "We find in him not only literary distinction but the love of piety. And that you may know how dear he is to us we have willed to give him this honorable testimonial of virtue and piety. And we further signify that every benefit you shall confer upon him will conduce to our gratification."

Galileo returned to his villa to complete what he had long dreamed of as the crowning work of his fruitful life. Even while he feared to ignore the Inquisition's warning, he had planned to set down in definitive form the results of his long study of Copernicus' theory and the discoveries which had convinced him of its truth.

While suffering from his painful illness and his fear of punishment from Rome, Galileo had been greatly encouraged and inspired by Thomas Campanella. This fearless warrior for freedom belonged to the Dominican order. At the University of Padua in 1595 he had matched Galileo in his attacks on the deadening influence of Aristotle. The Holy Office, alarmed by the iconoclast's boldness, threw him into prison, released him and then imprisoned him again for his alleged political plotting. He was tortured, then sentenced to death, but reprieved with the doubtful mercy of life imprisonment. After twenty-seven years in prison he was paroled by the Holy Office of the Inquisition and finally granted complete liberty.

But Father Campanella had never learned caution. He became involved in a conspiracy in his native Calabria and was forced to flee from Italy to France. Here Cardinal Richelieu not only gave him refuge but granted him a pension. Five years later the fugitive priest ended his stormy career by dying peacefully in a Dominican convent in Paris.

But while suffering in a Neapolitan dungeon Thomas Campanella had proved that liberty may often shine the brightest in a dark prison. There he began and completed his famous protest *The Apology for Galileo.* Smuggled past the captive's tormentors, the work was sent to Frankfort and published there in 1616.

Had this book merely defended him and his teachings, Galileo might have accepted it as one of many tributes. But this was a defense not only of the astronomer but of his scientific methods. The priest declared that arguments against the new science were really the result of ignorance of the scriptures. He denounced the arrogance of clerics "who now that they are called masters are ashamed again to become disciples"; he protested that "science is permitted to observe but the Church sits as the judge."

The martyr's plea for the method of investigation, which Galileo had done so much to introduce and further, touched the aging scholar deeply. In the dark years after the Inquisition's warning, he was especially inspired by Campanella's example. Yet even as he gloried in his defender's fearlessness Galileo wondered whether he would ever have the courage to follow him.

But I will be very, very cautious, he promised himself. If he takes sufficient care, a man may serve the truth and still avoid the dungeon and the stake.

The work which was to be the climax of all Galileo's achievements was finished at last. Because of the form in which he had cast his book, Galileo entitled it *Dialogue on the Two Chief Systems of Cosmology, those of Ptolemy and Copernicus.* He read and reread the bulky manuscript, now adding a phrase, now crossing out a sentence. By the time the task of revision was completed, Galileo's head swam with weariness. He brushed aside the waves of mist which for the last few days had danced before his eyes.

I need a long rest, he decided. When I am in Rome there will be no time to half-blind myself over my manuscript. Then my eyes will be as good as ever.

Since he knew the *Dialogue* would secure the most favorable reception if it were published in Rome, Galileo had long ago decided to submit the book to the Vatican's censors.

The invention of the printing press had done much to spread new ideas, often considered dangerous by the rulers of church and state. At this time censorship was not a prerogative claimed by the Church alone. William Shakespeare had always been most cautious in expressing his opinions on political and religious matters; yet in Protestant England he had been obliged to apply for a license before any of his plays might be printed. In Rome the Pope as the head of the independent papal state might forbid the publication of any work rejected by his board of censors.

Just what happened in Rome after the censors read the *Dialogue* is a long and confusing story. For centuries conscientious historians have disputed just what restrictions the censors in Rome placed upon the book and what corrections they demanded. Galileo's enemies later insisted that before he received the imprimatur of the Church's approval, Galileo promised to make all the desired changes. Galileo's supporters with equal violence declared he had practiced no deception.

Returing to Florence with the business still unsettled, Galileo corresponded frequently with the chief of the Roman Censorship Board. After many nagging delays extending for over a year, Galileo decided he would try to have the book published in Florence. He first submitted the manuscript to the officers of the local Inquisition which represented the state of Tuscany. After more delays and much correspondence with Rome, the inquisitorial board of Florence signed their approval; the list of names was headed by that of the chief of the papal censorship.

When the *Dialogue* was published at last in 1632, the greatest scholars in Europe wrote warm and enthusiastic letters to the author. Campanella, whose praise meant so much to Galileo, declared that "this renaissance of old truths . . . these new systems and these new ideas announce the beginning of a new epoch."

To Galileo, resting after his labors, this last triumph seemed to begin a new and happier chapter of his life. His great work, which he had so often feared he might not finish, had been given to the world. The record of his beliefs would live to enlighten mankind long after his tired body was hidden away in the family vault at Santa Croce. And now he could hope for a more personal immortality. His only son had married pretty little Sestilia shortly after he had graduated in law at Pisa. Galileo rejoiced in a grandson. The aging man prayed that the child someday would make even more illustrious the family name he himself had helped to make so honorable.

Galileo exulted over the letters which praised his latest book; those containing criticism, usually absurd or carping, he flung aside. I will no longer waste time and energy answering such attacks, he resolved. It is enough that my work has been hailed by the most responsible scholars as the outstanding book of our age.

But he wondered why no word had come from Rome. Of course, he reasoned, his friend Pope Urban and many of his close advisers were greatly occupied with the war. The victories of the Protestant general, King Gustavus Adolphus of Sweden, surely occupied the thoughts of the papal court. Many of the authorities in the Roman College might have been struck down by the terrible plague now sweeping over Italy. The confusion and fear the Pestilence created made communication difficult; because of the quarantine restrictions, it had been impossible for a while to send copies of the *Dialogue* to Rome. Even if the books had reached the scholars there for whom they were intended, their letters might be delayed or might never be delivered. Galileo shuddered to remember the story of the post-boy found mad and dying of the plague beside the road which led from Rome to Florence. In his last delirium the wretched messenger had torn to bits every letter from the empty bag which lay beside him.

One morning, bright with autumn sunshine, the scientist walked slowly beneath the trees in his garden. He grieved that he no longer was permitted to prune and dig. His physician had forbidden such effort after vainly trying to cure the aged man of a painful rupture.

Galileo sat down to rest on the mossy stone under his favorite olive tree. Here he decided to wait until the gardener's boy, sent early that morning to Florence to perform various errands, returned with the week's letters and news of Vincenzio. Galileo sighed a little. Thank God, the plague had so far spared Vincenzio, his wife and their little one! But would his son never grow up? He was not advancing in the minor position of a government clerk his father had secured for him. Foolishly extravagant, Vincenzio expected Galileo to pay his debts. He was no longer satisfied with the house his father had given him for a wedding gift. It would be very pleasant, Vincenzio hinted on his infrequent visits, to build a larger dwelling; then some of Sestilia's family for whom she was so lonely might come and live with them.

Galileo was roused from his painful thoughts by the click of the gate. The gardener's boy stood there, hesitating and uncertain. In spite of the growing dimness of his eyes, Galileo could see that the lad's hand was filled with letters.

"Why are you mooning there," Galileo asked him cheerily, "when the cook waits as impatiently for the kid and eggs she sent you to purchase as I wait to see what the post has given you?"

The youth approached Galileo and dropped the letters into the outstretched hand. Now his master noted that he was white and trembling. Was the servant trying to confess some fault for which he feared punishment? It must be a serious offense, thought Galileo, always too indulgent to his household. Perhaps the boy had disobeyed him and ridden the little white mule to town and lamed it on the road. Or—and the father's face also grew white—when the servant had inquired at Vincenzio's house, the doors had been sealed. Vincenzio, his wife, the precious grandson were dying of the plague!

"What has happened?"

The boy began to stammer in his terror.

"Master," he brought out the words painfully, "Master, I must tell you—"

"What of my son Vincenzio? What of his family?"

"I talked with his lady wife. She said that they were all well, praise be to God, and sent you their respects. But, Master, forgive me—!"

Galileo crossed himself. But though relieved he grew more impatient.

"Forgive you for what? You could not have lost your purse again for your basket is heaped high with provisions. If you dared ride and injure my little mule—"

"No, Master. It is something much more serious. Forgive me for being the bearer of evil tidings. In the market place, I met —I dare not repeat his name because if it were known he has been eavesdropping—"

"Never mind names! What evil tidings?"

"He saw this letter in my hand, the long one sealed with the papal seal. He can read no more than I, being but a servant of one of the inquisitors of Florence; but he knew the seal. Only yesterday he saw a letter on his master's desk; it had just arrived and bore that seal. And he heard his master say—"

"Take the cook her provisions," Galileo said, controlling his own mounting terror with difficulty, "and forget any idle gossip you heard in the market place."

The gardener's boy turned as though to obey. Then, seeing that his master was too absorbed in breaking the seal to observe him, he lingered behind the shrubbery. At last the old man finished reading the single page which he dropped upon the ground. He tried to rise, but his legs had grown so weak and trembling that he sank back upon the mossy stone.

Galileo's first thought was that now he would be parted for many months—if not forever—from Maria Celeste. Now established in the convent infirmary, she had overtaxed her frail body in caring for her many charges. Galileo knew that some of her patients had been stricken by the plague. If he left her he might not find her alive, even if he returned. The letter from the Holy Office commanded Galileo to appear without delay before the Inquisition at Rome.

THE DARKNESS OF THE PIT

GALILEO'S TERRORS AGGRAVATED his chronic illness. For weeks he tossed upon his bed, wracked with arthritis. Word came to his sickroom that the Florentine printer had been forbidden to print any more copies of the *Dialogue* until Galileo appeared in Rome and the court decided for or against him and his book.

The physician ordered complete rest. "Even if you are able to travel," he said, "it will be unsafe for you to risk such a long journey in this wet, bleak weather. The plague is still raging. If you leave your villa and mingle on the road with those who spread the disease, you may contract it. In your weakened condition you would surely die."

"Was not my summons to appear before the Inquisition my death sentence?" groaned Galileo. "Then why should I fear exposure to the plague? Why do you forbid me to appear before my enemies to defend myself?"

He tried to rise from his bed but fell back shrieking with pain.

"I do not forbid you," answered the physician. "Rather I say that your illness commands you to rest. Remember you are seventy years old and for years have been a sick man."

He called in two other prominent Florentine doctors for consultation. They agreed that it would mean certain death for Galileo to travel in his present condition. Together the three physicians appeared before the officers of the Inquisition in Florence. One of these local inquisitors wrote to Rome; he affirmed Galileo's willingness to face his judges but, repeating the medical report, pleaded for further delay. Another Florentine, Secretary of State Andrea Cioli addressed a letter to the authorities: "Poor Galileo is in bed and he runs the risk of going to another world rather than to Rome. God has said, 'I do not desire the death of a sinner.'"

Nor was the Inquisition anxious to have Galileo die before standing trial. The attack—personal and on his latest book—having been launched, the authorities desired to vindicate themselves. He was granted a short reprieve. But the suffering man did not need to be warned that a long delay would prove dangerous.

"Your persecutors desire nothing more than your actual absence from Rome," wrote Castelli, "in order to be able to agitate against you publicly and call you a rebel. . . . That is why I hope you will . . . make a great effort to overcome your weakness and set out in spite of the bad weather. . . . Commend yourself to God and come quickly, because I have every hope that you will overcome all difficulties."

Again Galileo tried to force his disease-wracked body into obedience. Since he knew he would never be able to endure the jolting of a coach, he gratefully accepted the grand duke's offer of a litter to carry him to Rome. Still in bed, he put his household affairs in order; wrote to his daughters since he could not have endured Maria Celeste's tears, even if he had been granted entrance into the plague-stricken infirmary; bade Vincenzio bring the little grandsons—there were two now—to the villa for a farewell visit. Leaning on a stout stick, the old man managed to hobble to his favorite chair before the fireplace, where he sat huddled for a few hours fighting against his weakness. But by the time Vincenzio arrived with his family Galileo was forced to return to bed.

The Holy Office had set the time for Galileo's hearing in October. The days, dreadful with uncertainty and pain, stretched into November. Now a gloomy Christmas dawned for the unhappy, bewildered scientist. Word came from Florence that Rome had issued orders, should there be further delay, to bring Galileo in chains to meet his accusers. This last ignominious threat did more to strengthen the sufferer than either the frantic pleas of his friends or the treatment of his physician. Galileo bade his servants dress him and carry him out to his litter.

For three long weeks he lay among the cushions, his mind tortured by his forebodings, his body torn with pain. The chill of the January rains and the bitterly cold wind from the Apennines seemed to cut into his very bones. Even for a younger man with an untroubled spirit and a robust body, the journey would have proved tedious. For Galileo it was a long, slow purgatory.

Since the plague still raged, Galileo was halted at the border of the papal state to be detained for some weeks in quarantine. He chafed at this further delay; his journey had so weakened him that he wondered whether he would ever reach Rome alive. He was so dazed and confused that when finally released he did not recognize at first the friend who waited to welcome him.

Francesco Niccolini, who sprang into the litter to grasp Galileo's hand on that January day in 1633, was the Florentine ambassador to the papal state. On several of Galileo's visits to Rome Niccolini had entertained him in his home and shown real affection for his distinguished guest. No fair-weather friend, he had refused to join those who deserted Galileo as soon as he fell under the displeasure of the Inquisition. The ambassador had often written to Grand Duke Fernando, urging the timid Tuscan ruler to use his influence to save Galileo. He had even risked Pope Urban's displeasure because, contrary to the rules of the Inquisition, he had attempted to discuss the forthcoming trial with him.

Now the ambassador took Galileo to the Florentine embassy, brought him to the luxurious apartment he had occupied on former visits and remained to see that the servants delegated to care for the old man made him comfortable. Stretched on the high, soft bed, as he sipped the heated wine Niccolini with his own hands had prepared for him, Galileo could no longer restrain his tears.

"You are as tender to me as though I were your father," he told Francesco Niccolini. "My own son has never shown me such care. Of all my family only Maria Celeste really loves me." He tried to rise. "Now I must send her word that I have arrived safely."

"I shall write her myself," promised the ambassador, gently pushing Galileo back upon the pillows. "But now you must rest." He nodded to a servant to draw the heavy damask curtains. "Try to sleep. Later when you feel stronger we will discuss what I have been able to learn concerning your trial."

"But why have so many of my old friends and supporters here turned against me?" Galileo puzzled the next day when Niccolini drew up a chair for him before the huge marble fireplace and seated himself on a low tapestried stool. "I know the Dominican scholars have been slow to acknowledge me;

they needlessly feel that my ideas will injure the prestige of
their Thomas Aquinas. But why have so many others joined in
denouncing me?"

Francesco Niccolini laughed sardonically.

"Why should a man of your wisdom, who has lived so long
in this world, ask such a naïve question? You were too successful during your visit here when cardinals and princes and great
scholars struggled to peer through your telescope. And why do
so many who have no interest in your science join your enemies?" Again he laughed bitterly. "When I was a small boy I
used to visit my old nurse's home in the country. One day I was
horrified to see not one but every chicken in the flock pecking at
a bleeding hen.

" 'Why do all of them try to kill that poor bird?' I asked my
nurse.

" 'My son,' I can remember her saying sadly, 'chickens are like
men. Whenever they discover one of their number in trouble
they all join to peck him to death.' "

"Perhaps you are right. But what puzzled me most are the
rumors that His Holiness has also turned against me. You know
that as a cardinal he honored me with his friendship, writing
verses in my honor, even signing his letters to me 'your affectionate brother.' But now—"

"Then the gossip concerning the Holy Father's change of
heart has not reached you in Florence?" interrupted Niccolini.
"I would hesitate to repeat such a silly lie; but that you may
the better defend yourself, you must know the story that is
being whispered in every corner of Rome. Remember, I myself
would never dream of accusing Pope Urban of stooping to
avenge a personal insult! But it is said that he feels that in
holding him up to ridicule you have committed a grave sacrilege
against the Church."

"I have never dreamed of casting ridicule upon Pope Urban!" cried Galileo hotly.

"Try not to excite yourself. You must grow strong to face what lies before you," warned his friend. "No such thought occurred to me when I first read the *Dialogue*. But one of your enemies, as clever as he is malicious, is said to have whispered in the Pope's ear that you used him for the model of the clownish Simplicio."

The charge seemed too ridiculous to credit; the more Galileo brooded over the accusation, the more he was shocked that Pope Urban could believe that he had been irreverently caricatured.

Galileo's latest and most controversial book had been cast in the form of dialogues between three very different characters. Remembering his promise to the Holy Office, the author tried to avoid directly attacking Ptolemy and his system; he attempted equally hard not to defend the views of Copernicus as established facts. The very title of the work shows how earnestly Galileo tried to maintain a neutral position: *Dialogue of Galileo Galilei,* Mathematician Extraordinary of the University of Pisa; Philosopher and First Mathematician of the Most Serene Grand Duke of Tuscany; where in meetings of four days are discussed the Two Principal Systems of the World, indeterminately proposing the Philosophical and Natural arguments, as well on one side as on the other.

Who were the three characters who in turn presented their "Philosophical and Natural arguments"? Salviati was drawn as a convinced follower of Copernicus; Sagredo represented the scholar of open mind, ready to consider from every angle every problem presented during the discussion. Simplicio, under whose name Galileo doubtless had described many of his opponents, repeated many of the arguments of the Aristotelians, whom Galileo had opposed even during his student days. How could any one honestly believe that his clownish conservative represented one particular follower of Aristotle!

"But it is absurd to say I had the Holy Father in mind!" Galileo protested. "Why should I, a good Catholic, hold him up to ridicule?"

Niccolini looked glum. "That is the very question I asked when this shocking charge was first repeated to me," he said. "Then I was given proof—"

"Proof!" shouted Galileo.

"If you will not listen calmly, I shall refuse to tell you anything more," warned the ambassador. "To me such 'proof' means nothing; I am your friend and prejudiced in your favor. But several of your enemies showed me the passage in which, they say, you put the very words of Pope Urban into the mouth of the fool—Simplicio."

Galileo was stunned. White with rage, he begged to be shown the offending passage. Niccolini rang for a servant and bade him fetch the volume. The huge tome was enclosed between covers of embossed leather, for Galileo had had a copy especially bound for his dear friend.

Pressing his dim eyes close to the page, Galileo found the fatal sentences. A reader, unless he were eager to stir up mischief, would have found nothing significant in Simplicio's statement concerning the supreme powers of God.

"His Holiness seems convinced that you have quoted him exactly," murmured Niccolini. "So if you have given the fool his words, maybe the whole character—"

"I swear by—by the life of my dear daughter that I never heard the Holy Father speak those words," interrupted Galileo. "No! Let me say rather that since I have been privileged to hold many long conversations with him, he may have made such a statement to me. But I have listened to many wise and holy men in my day and it may be I became confused. So if I am permitted to explain to my old friend—"

Niccolini held up a warning hand. "Not a word of what I have told you! Pope Urban would never acknowledge that his anger against your book has been stirred by personal feelings. Besides, he has positively refused to grant you an audience. Believe me, I have done all that I could do in your behalf. Now we can hope only that the prayers of your good daughter will cause God to soften the hearts of your judges."

"May I appear before them soon!" said Galileo heavily. "This suspense which I have borne so long is almost as bitter as death."

For two months Galileo waited in the ambassador's luxurious house. It had become his prison since he was forbidden by the court to leave it or to communicate with anyone in Rome except Niccolini. But his long rest gave him back something of his old strength. Sitting on the balcony to enjoy the grateful March sunshine, and rereading a tender note from Maria Celeste, it was easier to hope a little.

Here Niccolini found him, smiling over the young nun's assurance that not only she but everyone at San Matteo—from the Mother Superior down to the grizzled steward—prayed for the welfare of their absent friend.

"See what the post has just brought me," invited Galileo holding out the letter.

Niccolini read it slowly, as though to postpone speaking.

"You must answer this before you leave my house," he said. "Yes, you are to leave at once. The Holy Office has just summoned you."

"They will put me in prison!"

"The rules of the Inquisition demand that while actually under trial the accused must be housed in the Dominican

Monastery. You have often passed it—the large building next door to the Church of Santa Maria Sopra Minerva," continued Francesco Niccolini, trying to speak casually. "I will send one of my most trusted servants to attend to all your wants. I will be permitted to send you meals from my own table—also pens and paper that you may keep yourself occupied. You will not feel yourself a prisoner. Now promise me that you will try to be strong and fight bravely, not only for your own sake but for all the friends who love you."

Galileo did not answer. Those who appeared before the Holy Office were bound to keep its procedure secret. But certain details had leaked out and Galileo knew all of them: the accused was never confronted with those who bore witness against him. Often, as in a civil court, the most excruciating forms of torture were applied to force a confession. Remembering these things, he bowed his head and with trembling fingers tried to make the sign of the cross.

Although anything but luxurious, the apartment assigned to Galileo in the Dominican cloister was clean and light and not too suggestive of a prison. The door was not bolted so that the serving man—who slept just beyond the threshold—might hear his new master call to him in the night. Every day one of Niccolini's servants arrived from the embassy with a hamper stocked with wine and fruits and rich little cakes. But although he had relished these delicacies at Niccolini's table, the solitary old man now usually left them untouched.

The day after his arrival the scientist, leaning heavily on his servant's arm, staggered along the corridors which led into the council chamber of the Holy Office. Here Galileo faced the three black-robed judges who sat behind a long table. Noting the accused man's weakness, one of the inquisitors ordered the servant to draw up a chair for the old man and to leave the room. Now Galileo was entirely alone—without even this humble friend to comfort him. The prisoner raised his blurred eyes toward the large crucifix which hung behind the table. No, he was wrong. One Friend remained. Galileo's lips moved in prayer.

He tried to answer clearly every question his judges leveled at him with deadly monotony. But he was a sick old man; his mind, once nimble enough to grasp the stars, now faltered and grew confused. Yes, he had been warned not to spread in any way the teachings of Copernicus. No, he had not disobeyed this dictum and broken his pledged word by writing the *Dialogue*. He had tried to present the views of the proscribed astronomer not as facts but as a hypothesis. This fact, Galileo defended himself, had been recognized by the Roman censors; had not their representative granted the book the body's imprimatur?

But had he not promised the papal censors to make certain statements in the Preface that every reader might understand what followed was not a defense of Copernicus? Yes, he had so promised, answered Galileo, and he had tried to make the prescribed changes in the Preface. But why, he was asked, was the Preface printed in a different type from the body of the work itself? Was this intended to show it had no connection with the rest of the volume? Galileo replied that the pages of the Preface had been held so long in Rome by the censor that the material had arrived in Florence too late to be printed with the rest of his book; being printed later, it was set up in different type.

His head began to swim; his body trembled so violently that he had to clutch the arms of his chair to keep from falling to the floor. He had once seen several peasant boys pelting a lizard with rocks. Why had he not tried to stop them? His accusers were closing in on him, also; he could feel each question striking on his tired brain. When the session was finally over he could not rise from his chair. His servant and a Dominican lay brother carried him back to bed.

The next day brought further inquiries in the council chamber. Had not Galileo written thus and thus about tides? Yes, he admitted, he had so written in the *Dialogue*. Had he not been warned that the imprimatur would be withheld unless he changed that statement? But, countered the accused, the head of the Roman censors had seen, had passed. . . . Yes, and he had already been removed from office for his negligence. . . .

These hours of inquiry were terrible enough; but even more horrible were the periods of respite. Galileo would lie on his bed picturing the tortures the Holy Office had prepared for him. Only yesterday one of his judges, seemingly at the end of his patience, had spat out fiercely: "There are ways of making a stubborn heretic speak!" Surely, that meant. . . .

Galileo remembered that long ago in Padua he had once sat talking late into the night with a Dominican priest, a doctor of canon law. The Dominican had admitted that the Inquisition, like the secular court, had been known to make mistakes; but he had insisted that its regulations were both just and merciful. For example, the Inquisition forbade the application of torture to any suspect over the age of sixty.

"Of course," this authority had conceded, "occasionally even the servants of the Holy Office exceed their authority. I am afraid that sometimes we have judges who in their zeal for the truth are willing to forget certain limitations placed upon them."

Whether the unhappy prisoner was ever actually confronted with the instruments of the torture chamber has never been proved. But in his terror the accused construed a dreadful warning in the veiled threats of his judges.

Would they keep him here until Death released him? Galileo anguished. Or would his last days be spent in the dungeons of Castel Sant' Angelo, that grim pile of stone where Giordano Bruno had waited for the end? Galileo could picture that end with cruel clarity: the public square ringed with hostile faces; the clearing where the bound man stood upon the heaped-up embers; the sudden, inhuman shrieks from those proud lips rising above the flames. . . . "O merciful God, O Lady of Pity," cried Galileo, "do not let me think of such horrors or I shall go mad! Help me to remember my garden, my workroom, my observatory, the little bench beside the convent wall where my girl and I used to sit and talk together until the bell summoned her to prayer."

One night the terrified prisoner tried to forget his fears by recalling earlier, happier days in Rome. He remembered the warm welcome of the gentle Jesuit Father Clavius; the banquet where the noisy guests had trooped up to the tower to look through the telescope; the picture Pope Urban had given him painted by a celebrated artist. Suddenly Galileo recalled the murals of the cloister of San Marco at Florence. The painter Fra Angelico had been invited to Rome to decorate the private oratory of the pope, Nicholas V, and had died three years later.

Galileo on his last visit to Rome had visited the tomb of the Florentine artist. He had been buried in the church beside the cloister where Galileo now tossed sleeplessly. Wasn't the Latin epitaph said to have been composed by Pope Nicholas? Yes, and after a little difficulty Galileo recited the verses:

> "Appeles' fame was mine, 'twas naught to me
> Save that O Christ I gave all gain to thee;
> The Tuscan Flower-City gave me birth.
> My guerdon Heaven; my art I leave to earth."

Such memories calmed him. But toward the midnight hour when he had at last fallen into a troubled sleep, he often dreamed of Bruno's final agony. The serving man, hearing his master's screams, would hurry to his bedside.

"No, I require nothing," Galileo told him. "Go back to your pallet, my son, and rest. I am truly sorry my evil dreams have disturbed you."

Unable to fall asleep again, Galileo would try to force himself to think quietly and logically. Why should the Inquisition spend so much effort in trying to break the spirit of a true Catholic? He had never been a rebel like Bruno; he still called the Church his Mother. Surely a mother should understand the hearts of her children and, understanding, forgive!

The next morning brought another session in the council chamber with more accusations, more questions.

Had Galileo not been informed officially that the works of Copernicus were placed on the Index in 1616 and were therefore not to be studied by true believers? "Certainly," Galileo replied. But he had also been informed that the *Revolutions* of Copernicus—after certain minor corrections had been made— after four years' suppression was again permitted circulation. "But," cried one of the inquisitors, "the accused overlooks the nature of these corrections. These amendations removed the teaching of the motion of the earth as a definite opinion and stated such an idea as a mere hypothesis."

Galileo knew from their frequent and exact quotations that his three judges had carefully studied both the *Revolutions* of Copernicus and his own controversial *Dialogue*. He realized that they were shrewd enough to doubt the sincerity of his statements—written earlier and frequently repeated in this very council chamber. For Galileo had definitely presented the Copernican theory as the better of the two systems. Believing this, these representatives of the Holy Office seemed determined to silence the Florentine's teachings forever.

Some Catholic historians hold that the judges who tried Galileo exceeded their authority. The Inquisition had authority only in the matter of faith and morals, not science. Galileo's stubborn devotion to the teachings of Copernicus was not an offense against either faith or morals. Although these same historians consider the Church as infallible, they state that its human instruments may sometimes make mistakes. The Holy Office, although it was an arm of the Church, was no more invariably perfect in its judgments than a civil court.

But Galileo never questioned the right of his judges to badger and torment him. He drew no fine distinctions. The only questions he asked himself as he tossed restlessly on his bed throught the midnight hours were whether he had really sinned against his faith and what would be his punishment?

Yes, and Galileo tried to examine the facts with his customary scientific impartiality, was it not true that all-merciful Mother Church was often forced to act without mercy toward her disobedient children? Not only to preserve her own authority but even more for the erring sinner's salvation. Afflict the body that you may save the soul! Better by far the cleansing quick flames of the fire in the public square than the everlasting flames of Hell.

He believed that the Inquisition, which had already brought him so much suffering, was cruel only for love's sake. He must not forget that when he stood before his judges, Galileo warned himself again and again. He was no longer angry or defiant. If shown his faults he would be grateful for any penance laid upon him. Once sinfully proud, now he would try to welcome any punishment. He realized it would be severe; he was no obscure sinner but the most famous scientist in all Europe. He knew the Church feared his example might lead lesser scholars astray.

But he prayed there would be no public humiliation. It would be hard for his cloistered daughters, even harder for Vincenzio and his children. He had never been a dutiful son; but now Galileo dreaded to bring shame upon him and the innocent grandchildren.

Galileo had heard more than once that it was a common practice of the Holy Office to give a prisoner a sense of false security. He was not summoned to appear in the council chamber the next morning, but a member of the Holy Office visited the prisoner. Sitting beside Galileo's bed the judge became a sympathetic friend; he was no longer threatening nor accusing, but seemed only eager that the sinner should recognize and renounce his errors.

Such informal conversations lasted for hours. They were filled with pitfalls which Galileo soon grew too bemused to avoid. The weary victim knew it would be safer to remain silent. But although he was certain that any word he might utter could be construed to his undoing, he felt forced to answer his tormentor's arguments. For Galileo also knew that his silence would be held as evidence of his guilt.

Nightfall would bring at last the mercy of privacy in his own room. Galileo would try to eat his supper. He was never hungry but he usually managed to eat enough to please the solicitous servant.

"Master, you have not tasted a morsel of food all day. Try these delicious dried fruits the ambassador has sent you," urged the servant. "Or just a bit of the breast of pheasant."

"If I could only exercise a little my glutton's appetite might return to me," Galileo complained. "And you have spread before me enough dishes to satisfy a hungry plowman after a day's work. Sit down and help me empty these dishes."

"But, Master, I dare not."

"So you are too proud to break bread with a prisoner of the Holy Office?" Galileo tried to laugh.

"My master knows that is not the reason," protested the servingman. "But who am I that I should think myself worthy of sitting at the same table with the great Galileo!"

Galileo laughed again and for a moment his eyes were no longer weary as they looked across the years.

"I remember," he said, "when I first visited Rome. I was ragged, yes, and not too clean, for that morning when I tried to wash at a fountain it was not possible to remove all the dirt of the roads. Yet Father Clavius invited me to share his breakfast. It was the noblest feast I have ever tasted; he was as learned as he was charitable—and while we ate, his good talk strengthened me like wine." He spoke abruptly. "Now sit down and eat with me and let me hear no more of your nonsense."

After the table had been cleared, the servant helped his master to undress. Galileo was so nervously exhausted that he could not sleep. For a long time he tossed upon his bed tortured by his doubts and fears.

Three weeks, so filled with mental torture that they seemed three years to the hounded man, dragged to an end. If his judges had hoped to wear him down completely, they had succeeded. His growing panic burned in his veins like a fever. On the morning of the twenty-second day of his imprisonment, when Galileo was summoned for his session in the council chamber, he burst into tears and, sobbing like a child, clung to his devoted manservant's hand.

"I will not go to them again," he declared. "Go, beg my

judges to be merciful and to pass sentence upon me. I would rather die now than drag out a few more miserable months in such suspense and suffering."

But for a while—although Galileo's suspense tormented him —he was spared the suffering of further questionings. The Holy Office declared that while his case was being reviewed he might again rest undisturbed under Niccolini's custody in the Florentine Embassy.

For almost a month the old scientist was permitted to regain his strength under the ambassador's loving care. Galileo wrote often to Maria Celeste, whose letters never failed to bring him comfort. Although his eyes troubled him, he studied the books his host procured for him; in the cool of the evening the two friends sat for hours in the garden and talked of many things. But although Niccolini tried to assure his guest that if he were condemned the sentence would be a mild one, Galileo still tossed from side to side in the night watches. He was haunted by visions of the dungeon and even the stake.

In late June the summons came to appear again before the court of the Holy Office. As Galileo stepped from the litter Niccolini had provided for him he looked fearfully toward the building which had once been his prison. Crimson roses bloomed brightly across its forbidding walls. Galileo's eyes darkened at the omen. When he had first seen them in April the flowers had glowed in their early beauty. Now, full blown, they scattered their red petals on the tiled path. There seemed to be a pool of blood at his feet. He drew back in horror at the omen and convulsively grasped his servant's arm.

"Courage, Master, it will soon be over," said the manservant.

The late June weather had grown intolerably hot and muggy. Galileo was grateful when a Dominican brother bade him sit and rest in the cool corridor. He was given a document to read and glanced over it, hardly knowing what he read. When he had finished he grew so white that the servant again whispered encouragement.

A few moments later Galileo stood before a great assemblage of cardinals, bishops, canons and monks to have sentence passed upon him.

Forcing himself to walk almost erectly, the old man made his way to the table where the judges of the Holy Office sat. Upon the table two tall candles shed their light over a large Bible. One of the judges rose to read a summary of the entire trial.

Sentence followed sentence, paragraph followed paragraph, page followed page. The passionless voice repeated question after question, answer after answer. Galileo swayed in his weakness but now he was not granted the mercy of resting in a chair. He clutched the edge of the table and prayed that his agony of mind and body would soon be over.

He listened to the accusations he had heard again and again during the past two months from those stern, tight lips: his sin of heresy for adhering to the theories of Copernicus, which he had dared to state as facts; his disobedience to Holy Church in his persistence in spreading such theories. . . . Finally came the sentence:

"We declare that the book entitled *Dialogue of Galileo Galelei* be placed under the public interdict; while as to you, we sentence your person to imprisonment in the charge of this Holy Office, for a term which we ourselves shall decide; and as a penance you are enjoined to repeat the seven penitential psalms every week for three years."

Galileo was then asked whether he was willing to renounce his errors. He nodded vaguely, scarcely aware of the action. If he could only escape from all these faces . . . stretch out his aching legs upon his bed . . . rest for a little while . . . sleep. . . .

"Then down on your knees and place your hand on this Bible."

With difficulty Galileo eased himself to his knees. A Dominican friar lowered the Bible that the old man might lay his hand upon it. Another attendant of the court handed the scientist a scroll.

There was a dull pounding in Galileo's ears; through it the cold hard voice he had just listened to so long sounded again:

"You have already been permitted to read this document. Now read slowly and loudly that all may hear the recantation this court has prepared for you."

For a moment Galileo's eyes blurred above the dancing letters. Frowningly he peered closer. A brown-robed Franciscan, believing that the condemned man found it difficult to decipher the writing in the growing dusk, took one of the candles from the table and held it close to the parchment. The friar's face was sweet with pity. He dropped his free hand upon Galileo's shoulder as though to comfort him.

"Thank you, Father," murmured Galileo. Falteringly he began to read his recantation:

"I, Galileo Galilei, son of the late Vincenzio Galilei, seventy years of age and a citizen of Florence, being a prisoner and on my knees, and before Your Eminences, having before my eyes the Holy Gospel, which I touch with my hand, abjure, curse and detest the error and the heresy of the motion of the earth."

THE SETTING SUN

IF SHAME COULD kill a man, Galileo Galilei would have died that night.

Before he was summoned to receive his sentence Galileo had been ordered to read his ignominious recantation. When, dazed with weariness, he had repeated the hateful words before the court, he had been conscious of only one affirmation: his false denial of Copernicus. Now, tossing on his bed, he recalled how he had committed a sin even more frightful than perjury.

With his hand on the Bible he had sworn to continue to deny his "errors and heresies and all such teachings inimical to Holy Church." Most shameful of all, he had pledged: "Should I meet a heretic or one to be suspected of heresy, I shall denounce him to the Holy Office or the local inquisitor or bishop." Now he realized that he had not only betrayed what he would always secretly believe to be the truth; he had sworn to aid in the persecution of his devoted followers. The Inquisition had done more than make Galileo its lifelong prisoner; it had sentenced him to become its spy.

146

Even more than his own condemnation Galileo mourned the condemnation of everything for which he had fought since his youth. The Holy Office, he knew, would do more than ban the publication and distribution of his books; it would proscribe the teaching of his ideas in every church university and punish any daring scholar who ignored the edict. Yes, he thought, it would have been better to have died than to linger on to see my beliefs suppressed and others suffer for my cowardice.

Becoming his own judge, Galileo through the night watches sought to justify his cowardice. He could say honestly that it was not only the fear of a horrible death that had prompted his recantation. He knew that if he were condemned to die as a heretic his property would be confiscated. It had brought him so much happiness that he had at last acquired enough wealth to satisfy even the greedy Vincenzio.

Poor little boy! thought Galileo as his mind slipped back through the years and he recalled his son as a round-faced child begging for a toy or sweetmeat. With the gold I hope to leave him he will not remain a government clerk. Perhaps a post in the diplomatic service—in time a title. How dared I rob him of his inheritance and leave him no legacy but a blackened name?

Galileo shuddered to think that if he had not recanted he would have been denied all the rites of the Church. How dreadful to drag out his last miserable years beyond the pale, cut off from the blessings of confession and communion, denied the blessed assurance of extreme unction and Christian burial. Mother Church had condemned and chastised him; yet he was still certain that without her ministrations he would be like an orphaned child crying in the darkness.

The old man sat up in his bed. Tears streamed down his withered cheeks. "God, forgive me for I have sinned!" he moaned, as he beat his shrunken breast. Then, lowering his voice, as though he feared that the servant sleeping on the threshold might hear his affirmation: "But, God of all the worlds, surely it is not necessary to tell Thee that the earth does move!"

The next day a new life—or rather a cloudy life-in-death—began for Galileo.

While the fate of his court mathematician hung in the balance, the grand duke, Fernando II, had hesitated to come to his defense. But as soon as the wretched old man was cleansed of heresy, his patron ventured to risk the Church's displeasure by pleading for clemency for its prisoner. He joined Niccolini and a few of Galileo's influential friends who appealed to Pope Urban to soften the sentence of the Holy Office.

Pope Urban was pleased to be merciful. In July the Inquisition permitted Galileo to leave Rome with all its shameful memories. He was to enjoy at least comparative freedom in the palace of his young friend Ascanio Piccolomini, Archbishop of Siena.

In the magnificent dwelling of his host's family that had given to Italy generals and saints, archbishops, cardinals and even a pope, Galileo began to feel less broken and humiliated. Nominally he was still in the custody of the Church, as represented by the kindly archbishop. But everybody in the household—from Piccolomini down to his youngest page—treated him with the courtesy due an honored guest. It comforted him in those days to read and reread a note from Maria Celeste:

"I wish," she wrote, "that I could describe the rejoicing of all the mothers and sisters on hearing of your happy arrival at Siena. On hearing the news, Mother Abbess and many of the nuns ran to me, embracing me and weeping for joy and tenderness."

Brought low in his humiliation, he wrote his daughter: "My name is erased from the book of the living."

To which she answered, seeking to comfort him: "Indeed you are loved and esteemed here more than ever."

Although she had never been burdened with the care of her own worldly possessions, Maria Celeste kept a careful eye on Galileo's villa and garden during his absence. She tells the exile how she has kept a strict account of the fruit sold, of the damage suffered by the vines from hail and thieves. Then she tries to cheer her homesick father by repeating the reports she has received from his gardener:

"My lady mule," she informs Galileo, "will carry no one else since her master is absent. There are two pigeons in the dovecote waiting for you to come and eat them; there are beans in the garden waiting for you to gather them." But sometimes a wistful note creeps through her gaiety. "When you were in Rome, I said to myself, If he were but at Siena. Now you are at Siena, I say, Would he were at Arcetre. But God's will be done!"

Another letter suggests that the poor who depend on the convent's bounty for their daily bread need his help. She describes with gentle pity the lingering illness of Sister Maria Silvia, said to have been the loveliest girl seen in Florence for three hundred years, now dying of consumption in her twenty-second year. Of her own growing weakness Maria Celeste never complains. But at last the courage of even this valiant saint forsakes her. She cries despairingly that she prays she will see her dearest father once more before she dies.

That prayer was granted. Archbishop Piccolomini and others with influence in the papal court urged that the exile be permitted to return to Arcetre that he might be near his children. The request was granted but with certain degrading conditions: Galileo must never visit Florence without special permission; at Arcetre he might leave his house only to attend Mass at the convent of San Matteo and to visit his daughters; he was forbidden to entertain friends or to "allow the assemblage of many at a time," a prohibition which made it impossible to give even informal scientific lectures. Galileo felt like a mouse released for a moment from beneath the paw of a hungry cat. He did not need to be warned that the inquisitors of Florence would watch his every action and report his slightest disobedience to Rome. But now he could think of nothing but his reunion with Maria Celeste.

When Galileo sent her a message that after five months' detention he was permitted to return home, her answer frightened him. She seemed too weak even to express the joy which he knew swelled her faithful heart. "I do not think I shall live to see that hour," she wrote, "yet may God grant it, if it be for the best."

Only her iron will kept the flame of life flickering in her enfeebled body until one bleak January day when they sat together once more in the reception room of San Matteo. Under her bulky habit her body had shrunk like a very old woman's; Death had set his seal on her ashen lips. But her eyes still glowed with their old tenderness. For a little while they talked of many things; but suddenly they both fell silent and neither spoke again until the bell sounded for evening prayers.

"Pray for me, child, for I sadly need your prayers."

"I always pray for you, Father," she answered and turned away quickly as though she dared not look upon his tears.

A few weeks later Sister Maria Celeste was carried to her

resting place among the sleeping nuns of San Matteo. She was only thirty-three but she was old in sorrow.

For days Galileo wandered through the villa, which had never seemed so lonely before. He felt no desire to visit his remaining daughter. The years had turned the sullen girl into a coldly self-righteous woman; she had never loved her sister and now she could not share Galileo's grief. When Vincenzio came from Florence to visit his father he was little better as a comforter. He could talk of nothing but his own affairs: the cost of the grand new house he wished to build, the miserable salary he received as a government clerk. Although Vincenzio never asked outright for money, Galileo suspected the reason for his visits.

Once after the old man had given him a goodly sum to help straighten his tangled finances, Vincenzio seemed actually stirred by a feeling of sympathy for the bowed figure huddled before the fire.

"Perhaps in time," he encouraged, "you may be allowed to return to Florence. There you will be more comfortable in our new house with the three children to amuse you."

"It will be in Florence as in Arcetre," Galileo answered him heavily. "I hear her constantly calling me."

Vincenzio hurried home to tell his wife that he feared the aged man was going mad.

But old and broken as he was, Galileo was still able to turn in his grief to what had always been his greatest solace—his work.

His fading eyesight prevented him from using his telescope. And even if I could spy out new wonders, he thought bitterly, what would any discovery mean to me or the world if I were forced to keep my records hidden? Walking in his garden one day in early spring, he was seized with an idea that made him happy for the first time since his daughter's death. He might no longer teach. If he published a single sentence on astronomical subjects which seemed to suggest he had not been sincere in his recantation and still favored Copernicus, the clutch of the Inquistion would tighten upon his shoulder. But if he wrote on an entirely safe subject. . . . It was only by accident that he had become the greatest astronomer of his age. What of his early interest in mechanics . . . the swaying pendulum . . . the weights dropped from Pisa's tower years ago?

Again he decided to set down his ideas in dialogue form, a device borrowed from the Greek philosophers. Employing the same three disputants, the author set them to discussing not astronomy but the safer subject of physics. At great length Galileo explained his ideas on the laws of falling bodies, on energy, on heat, on specific gravity. He would not have written so calmly had he been able to foresee that in the same year of his death, but eleven months later, a child would be born in England to continue the never-ending search for truth. Nikolaus Copernicus, Galileo Galilei, Isaac Newton . . . the torch drops from the hand of the tired runner to be carried farther by one who takes his place!

Galileo called this work—the summing up of his many years of experimentation—*Dialogues Concerning Two New Sciences*. In an outburst of his youthful enthusiasm he wrote to a friend that this book was "superior to everything else of mine hitherto published . . . [since it contained] results which I consider the most important of all my studies."

Since Galileo had been condemned by the Inquisition, this work of his sunset years could not be published either in Rome or Florence. But Louis Elzevir of the Low Countries, an admirer of Galileo, managed to visit him and took the manuscript back with him to Holland where it might be safely printed.

Perhaps I will not be spared to hold a copy in my hands, thought Galileo. He remembered the story that Copernicus had smiled when his book, the child to insure him immortality, lay upon his dying pillow.

But by 1637 the printing was completed. Galileo, to escape censure from the Holy Office, denied that he had had anything to do with publication of the manuscript, which, he said, he had permitted a few scientists to read. Fortunately for the rebel his old enemies in Rome were far too occupied with the Thirty Years' War to interest themselves in his disobedience. Those who read the book could find nothing to condemn, so the Inquisition decided to ignore it.

"A pity that the Holy Office should make a sneak and liar of an honest man," Galileo chuckled with something of his youthful impudence.

But now he was struck down by a calamity crueler than any punishment his persecutors could devise for him.

Slowly, painfully, he dictated a letter to Elia Diodati, a liberal Protestant living in Paris, who had served Galileo and science by distributing copies of the *Two Systems* throughout the Protestant world:

"In reply to your kind letter of November 20, 1637, in which you inquire about my health, I must tell you that my strength has improved, but, oh, my esteemed sir, Galilei, your devoted friend and servant, is now completely and incurably blind. The sky, the earth, the universe, which I have enlarged a hundred and a thousand times beyond the known limits of the past centuries, by wonderful observations and clear deduction, is shrunk to the narrow space which I myself fill in it. So it pleases God; it shall therefore please me also."

Father Castelli, the distinguished mathematician, was sorely grieved over this last affliction which had overtaken his revered master.

"The noblest eye which nature ever made is darkened," ran his tribute, "an eye so privileged and so gifted with rare qualities that it may with truth be said to have seen more than the eyes of all who are gone and to have opened the eyes of all who are to come."

A man of action, the priest was not satisfied merely to condole with his afflicted teacher. Letters begging that Galileo be permitted to go to Florence and receive needed medical treatment had already been addressed to Rome from many influential persons. These pleas had been answered with the curt suggestion that it was not too difficult for a physician to journey to Arcetre and the warning that frequent petitioning would only increase the rigor of Galileo's punishment.

Still at this crisis Castelli dared to make another appeal to the Holy Office that the ailing prisoner be allowed to live in his son's house in Florence. A medical certificate describing the aged man's condition, also the news of his blindness, finally persuaded those who had condemned Galileo that he need no longer be feared. But before Galileo was brought to the fine new house on the Castra San Giorgio, he was obliged to appear before the officers of the Florentine Inquisition.

Here he was told that he would not be allowed to leave his son's home except to attend Easter Mass at the nearest church. ("My dear little girl, now I will be too far away to visit your grave!") He must never discuss the Copernican theory with anyone. (Too late, the *Dialogue* which the Inquisition has helped to make famous is read by every liberal scholar in Europe!) He must not receive any visitors whom the Holy Office suspected of heretical opinions. If these commands were ignored, Galileo was warned, he would end his days in prison under the ban of excommunication.

The old scientist listened meekly, promised to obey the wishes of the Holy Office and departed—leaning heavily on Vincenzio's arm.

What hurt him most was the knowledge that his son, who had been appointed his guardian, was really a spy of the Inquisition. He knew that Vincenzio would be zealous in his supervision. The poorly paid clerk, always in debt, had no intention of allowing his father to incur the Church's further displeasure. This would mean the loss of the pension the grand duke allowed Galileo during his lifetime and the confiscation of Galileo's property after his death. As an expectant heir, Vincenzio had no intention of forfeiting a small fortune.

Galileo, long used to his son's neglect, now was forced to bear his autocratic manner. He turned for companionship to Sestilia; however, his daughter-in-law, busy with household cares, seemed to have no time to listen to what she considered the ramblings of a doddering old man. But children still loved Galileo, and his three grandsons left their games to listen to his stories. They begged him to play his lute for them and added their gay voices to his faltering tenor, when he tried to teach them a favorite song.

Once he began the melody he had composed so long ago:

"I have sought through Calabria,
    Lombardy and Tuscany,
Rome, Pisa, Lucca, Genoa,
    All between sea and sea. . . ."

He broke off suddenly, then burst into tears.

"Go on, go on, it's such a pretty tune!" cried the three little boys.

Galileo shook his white head. "I have forgotten the rest," he lied.

"Then sing that part over again," the children pleaded.

"No, I am too tired. Go and play before the sun sets and your mother calls you in for supper."

They dashed out into the courtyard, laughing and shouting. Galileo put aside his lute and sat alone—weeping in his darkness.

Doubly a prisoner, he tried to save himself from madness by recalling his many discoveries and inventions.

That section on falling bodies I described in my last book, he mused. Who would have thought that my first crude experiments with the pendulum . . . how that physician in Pisa praised my pulsifier . . . didn't he pay me a stoop of wine for it? . . . A miniature pendulum . . . a clock to measure the time ticking in a sick man's pulse . . . a pendulum . . . a clock. . . .

His weak hands itched to create what his still active brain had already begun to devise.

One day he mentioned the matter to Vincenzio.

"If one were able to attach a pendulum to an ordinary clock," he suggested, "it would become much more accurate. There is the matter of balance, and—but I will explain all that to you later. Since there are no pendulum clocks on the market, there should be a fortune in such an invention," he added shrewdly. He knew that Vincenzio would never be deaf to any idea that might fill his yawning purse.

"But how can you work on it now?" asked Vincenzio.

"If you would call in a clever mechanic, I could—"

"And have him steal your ideas!" interrupted Vincenzio scornfully. "Pardon me, Father, but you have never been a businessman. No—when I can spare the time you can tell me how to proceed and I will draw the necessary diagrams. Then I will consult some craftsman, give him only one idea at a time, have him advise me—and construct the clock myself."

Galileo was doubtful of the plan, but he knew that his son could not be persuaded to hire an assistant. It became harder than ever to induce Vincenzio to act as secretary when it was necessary to dictate letters. The correspondents might be the leading scientists of Europe, but Vincenzio felt he had no time for them. He was eager to spend every spare moment discussing the pendulum clock; he must have a completed model before the inventor died.

If I might only employ a secretary, Galileo thought. Not only to attend to my huge correspondence but to listen intelligently to the thoughts of a forgotten scholar. One of my old pupils! But I dare not engage any disciple who might be suspected by the Inquisition. What will become of a new idea that has just captured my mind if it is not set down before it is lost forever?

At last the Florentine inquisitors announced that they had found a scientist who could be trusted to act as Galileo's secretary. To Galileo's delight the young man was well equipped to work with him on his latest project, which concerned navigation.

The youthful Renieri was more gratified to work with the neglected genius than he dared allow the Holy Office to suspect. Although the secretary might not express his opinion openly, he believed that the day would come when Galileo and the scientific truths for which he suffered would be vindicated. Galileo knew again the reverence and affection he had once received from his pupils. Best of all, Renieri was far enough advanced in his studies to prove a prop when the older man's usually keen mind grew bewildered.

"I am obliged to have recourse to other hands and other pens than mine since my loss of sight," Galileo laments in one of his letters. "My memory is impaired by advanced age and many a time I am forced to have the foregoing sentences read to me before I can tell what is to follow; else I would repeat the same thing over and over." He adds ruefully: "Take my word for it, that between using one's own eyes and hands and those of others there is as great a difference as in playing chess with one's eyes open or blindfold!"

But the devoted Renieri was as patient as he was skillful in untangling any confused dictation. A genuine affection sprang up between the two, quickly noted by Vincenzio. He became violently jealous; one day he accused his father of sharing the secret of the pendulum clock with the secretary.

"Sometimes I wonder whether you are really my son," Galileo told him, his voice rising in anger, "with your stupid brain and even more stupid hands. Faugh! when I was younger than your first-born I turned out little engines with wheels and pulleys for my sisters to play with. Continue to tinker; it is a safer occupation for you than gambling in the tavern. I swear to you I will not share the idea with Renieri or any living soul. It happens I am much more interested in these ideas on navigation which—but you wouldn't understand."

But Vincenzio continued to spy on his father and the secretary. At last Galileo became so outraged that he appealed to the Holy Office to allow him to return to Arcetre.

"I came to Florence that I might receive medical aid," he said. "But now I know that no physician can help me. I would spend the last days that are left to me in my villa. I want to walk in my garden again and visit the grave of my beloved child."

"But who will care for you?" asked one of the inquisitors.

"My secretary, who has become my son."

The jealous Vincenzio threatened to warn the Holy Office that his father could not be trusted even a short distanct from Florence. But Sestilia interposed.

"I am weary of all this wrangling," she complained. " 'A house where there is constant quarreling even if it be as large as the Forum at Rome grows too small,' " she quoted the proverb. "Let the old man go in peace and promise to visit him often."

So Vincenzio made no more objections and Galileo was permitted to return to Arcetre. He was able to rehire several of his faithful servants; Renieri nursed him tenderly. The secretary carried a heavy burden; but soon it was divided with another youth—Viviani, who appeared one morning and begged to be allowed to serve Galileo without wages.

Viviani, Galileo was interested to learn, like himself had come from a noble Florentine family now fallen on evil days. The boy had studied mathematics with a Franciscan who, having taught him all he knew of the science, urged him to ask Galileo to accept him as a pupil.

Galileo could not teach him openly. But often when they were together during the long, sleepless nights, the two discussed mathematics. The old man rejoiced in his renewed contact with a brilliant young mind. He was not one to praise a pupil extravagantly, but once in a burst of enthusiam he told Viviani:

"I wish some of the complacent savants who condemned me in Rome had the knowledge of geometry which is yours—before you have actually grown a beard. You will go far in your field, but," and he sighed, "I shall not be here to rejoice in your success."

Either of the devoted disciples could have worked with Galileo on his pendulum clock; but he remained true to his promise to Vincenzio.

The would-be inventor, however, grew more and more suspicious. Now he came to see his father several times a week; he usually brought Sestilia with him, leaving her to guard the door that no one might listen to his report on the clock's progress.

"Why are you so eager to finish it?" Galileo once asked him with an indulgent smile. "I have never known anything to hold your interest so long."

"I know you think I am only an indifferent government clerk," Vincenzio explained with unusual gentleness. "I know, also, how it hurts you that I, your only son, have never won any honor while you have been so greatly esteemed. But if I succeed with this invention, you will at last be proud to call me your son."

"My dear boy," said Galileo, grimly amused, "may your sister who is surely a saint in heaven intercede for you. For you are even a greater liar than I am."

Fortunately Vincenzio was so disarmed by Viviani's modesty and charm that he did not trouble to quarrel with him. He did not question the stranger's presence in the villa, while the assurance of the grand duke quieted any fears the Holy Office might have entertained of the youthful stranger. For now that he no longer imperiled his own soul by defending a heretic, Fernando treated his old court mathematician with unfailing kindness. He sent wine from his own cellars and rare fruits to tempt the invalid's appetite. Soon the gilded ducal coach rumbled up the winding road to Galileo's villa. Naturally the Inquisition had no desire to curb His Highness' visits. No one had ever suspected the grand duke of being capable of discussing scientific matters with Galileo—or anybody else.

So the weak-kneed but kindly ruler often graced Galileo's sickroom with his presence, chatting of the latest battle of the never-ending war or of trivial happenings in his court. Once when Viviani reminded Galileo that it was time for his medicine, the grand duke insisted on giving him the draught with his own royal hand. Sestilia, who was spending the day at Arcetre, already had been flustered by the monarch's visit. Now she shrieked to her children to come in from the garden to witness the honor being shown their grandfather.

Whereupon the visitor uttered the only sensible words which, according to history, ever fell from the royal lips:

"I have only one Galileo," he explained away his condescension.

Another visitor, who might have been forbidden to see Galileo had Vincenzio been sufficiently alert, was a young English poet who introduced himself as John Milton.

Later, when questioned, Viviani described him to his master:

"He is not tall—but well proportioned and he carries himself with ease and grace; you remember he told us that at college he was a skillful swordsman. His long hair, which is light brown, he wears parted and falling to his shoulders. He has the complexion we have learned to expect in young Englishmen, fair and unblemished. I think I shall always remember his eyes —dark gray, clear and as piercing as an eagle's."

"Itemized like a true mathematician!" commented Galileo. "You say he has an eagle's eyes?" He was silent for a long time; when he spoke the secretary had to bend nearer to catch his words. "So were mine once. May God forbid that he should ever know what it is to be caged and to live in darkness."

For a too brief hour the old scientist and the young poet talked together while the two secretaries listened respectfully in the background. In return for several of Galileo's racy stories of his student days at Pisa, which the traveler had just visited, the Englishman described his own studies at Christ's College, Cambridge. He had recently lost his best friend, whose death had inspired the elegiac poem "Lycidas."

"You were fortunate to be able to put your sorrow into words," said Galileo. "When I was young I, too, wrote verses; some I fear were scandalous, all were light. When my sainted daughter died I wished that I might honor her with an elegy or at least a sonnet. But I, alas, have never been a true poet."

With his ever-ready courtesy Galileo turned the conversation back to the stranger's own writings. What other poems had he written? What work did he contemplate when he returned from his trip through Italy?

"I have written a masque, sir, called *Comus,* which has been performed by the nobility, not without success. In it, as a Puritan, I try to teach how the powers of evil in the end must be conquered by purity and goodness."

"A doctrine to which I, as a Catholic, subscribe," Galileo prodded him slyly.

"Surely; for though there are far too many battling creeds in the world today, still there is only one moral law," the young man answered rather pompously. Then, as though fearing it might seem that he was delivering a preachment to his elder, he said warmly: "Before I leave, sir, because I have but a little while in Florence and there is so much to see, I want to thank you for your help and inspiration."

"Surely, you are not a scientist as well as a poet," said Galileo.

"No, my studies at Cambridge were chiefly devoted to the classics; but I also studied music and modern languages."

"That is why you speak Italian so musically and do not butcher it like most foreigners."

"It is good of you to say so, sir. I have taken pains for I consider Italian the loveliest of all tongues. No, I cannot claim to be even an amateur scientist. But I have read something of your writings and heard wiser men than I discuss them. And"—his voice deepening with feeling—"I have looked through your telescope.

"I wish I might write an ode on the thoughts which came to me that night," went on John Milton. "I felt that I stood with the Creator Himself and with Him watched the wonders of creation appear to mortal man for the first time."

Galileo nodded, much touched with the tribute.

"A magnificent thought which might be forged into a mighty poem," he said. "Or Adam in Paradise looking up at the stars for the first time!"

The visitor rose to clasp Galileo's hand.

"I hope I have not stayed too long and tired you, sir." He spoke with forced cheerfulness. "If I ever write a poem on the subject, I will try to render it into Italian and send it to you."

John Milton could not dream that it would be a quarter of a century before—in his own blindness—he would dictate *Paradise Lost* to his daughters, with its many allusions to the Copernican system. But when his eagle eyes rested on Galileo's face he saw death scrawled across the worn features, and it was hard to speak lightly.

Galileo himself knew that his prison doors would shortly open and he was glad. In spite of the warm companionship of his disciples, he grew increasingly lonely.

Shortly after Milton's visit a third scholar joined the small and illegal university at Arcetre, bringing much comfort to its head. Torricelli had done considerable research in physics and had already published several books. As the newcomer enthusiastically outlined his brilliant ideas for improving the thermometer, Galileo's useless arthritic fingers twitched and his face darkened with envy. But when he spoke, there was no envy in his voice, only a deep sadness for his own helplessness.

"A new thermometer? An improvement on the one invented by Robert Fludd, the Englishman? That I cannot praise, since he based his thermometer on my earlier one and forgot to give me credit."

"When did you work on the thermometer, Master?"

"So long ago that it seems a hundred years! Let me think—it was in those blessed days when my fingers could hardly keep up with my brain. The microscope—other inventions—often I tinkered with first one, then another; I seldom finished them."

"Tell me about your thermometer," the younger man urged eagerly.

"I sealed the top of one arm of a U-tube and partly filled it with water," Galileo recollected. "The water poured into the open end, trapped some air at the top of the sealed arm. When the temperature rose, this trapped air expanded and pushed the water down. When the temperature fell, the air contracted and the water rose. The volume occupied by the trapped air—as indicated by the water level—was the measure of the temperature."

The aged scientist sighed. "I'll wager you a flagon of the grand duke's best wine, young sir, that you never heard of my invention. How could you, when I was too busy to market the model; yes, even too occupied to describe it except in several long-forgotten letters to fellow scientists. No matter! Now tell me your ideas." Galileo spoke with courteous interest, but his slight effort had tired him and he wondered whether he would be able to concentrate on the inventor's words.

"I am experimenting by using mercury instead of water, since mercury will not freeze or evaporate in ordinary temperatures," answered Torricelli.

"Good!" murmured Galileo.

Torricelli in his enthusiasm began to speak of his work with the barometer,

"I remembered Aristotle's theory that 'Nature abhors a vacuum.' That helped to explain why the mercury I used in the tube, instead of water, always rose. I noted that the height of the mercury varied from day to day." Torricelli laughed. "I reasoned that Nature would not act like a flirtatious girl and show a different horror to the tube's vacuum on different days. So I was forced to discard Aristotle's notion and concluded that the variations in the mercury's height must be due to atmospheric pressure."

He ended triumphantly; during his explanation he had been idly drawing a rough sketch. Now, receiving no answer, he glanced up and noticed forgivingly that the greatest scientist in Europe had fallen asleep.

Much as the young men loved him, Galileo yearned for the affection of his own flesh and blood. He was no longer allowed to visit his daughter, who took no pains to keep in touch with him. From far off Munich came word that his brother Michelagnolo, his wife and several of their children were dead.

I should have tried to be more patient with all of them when they visited me here, Galileo accused himself. But I shall see them shortly.

He asked for a notary and drew up his will. Galileo bequeathed a small annual sum to Sister Archangel; he knew she needed nothing, but this last gesture might remind the bitter, aloof woman that he had not forgotten her. The remainder of a not inconsiderable fortune Galileo left to his son. And he requested burial as near as possible to the tombs of his parents in his favorite church, Santa Croce.

As the notary guided the shaking signature to the document, Galileo's throat filled with sobs. If he might only look once more on the masterpiece of another lonely old man, he thought, recalling the gracious figure of the Virgin bending over her dead son.

He sank back exhausted on his pillows. His universe, which had shrunk to a dark room, would soon diminish to an even smaller cell. Smaller than the cell in which Maria Celeste had so often knelt to pray for him; almost as small as her last crowded resting place. He knew she was not there. She was safe in some celestial sphere no human eye would ever pierce, interceding for him in her peaceful paradise. Paradise! From where Beatrice, beloved of Dante, shone upon the troubled Florentine's soul like a lovely star and brought him comfort. His Maria Celeste was like Beatrice; not so beautiful, for who could be so lovely?—but like her in tender, undying devotion. Then how could he be afraid?

Inquiries and good wishes began to pour in from the court, from all the great ones of Florence. From Rome itself Pope Urban sent his papal blessing to the friend he had loved—and deserted in his need. Galileo did not seem to listen while Vincenzio read the parchment with its unique seal, laying it carefully aside as a proud heritage for his sons. But when Sestilia leaned over the bed to whisper whether she should send for a priest, her father-in-law seemed to understand. For he nodded eagerly as though he were glad to be permitted the last, comforting rites of the Church.

The month was January, the year 1642. Protestants and Catholics were still struggling and dying on the scattered battlefields of Europe. And in Italy a tired warrior in his seventy-eighth year fought his last grim fight against death.

Galileo's gnarled hands, once so subtle, tugged at the bed covering with something of their old strength; his eyes widened until Vincenzio drew back afraid. For a moment it seemed to him that his father could really see again.

But to the dying man the room was still heavy with a darkness that he could not penetrate. He was thinking, now that the priest had left him shriven and forgiven, that it was time for him to die. But he was not yet ready.

Is one ever ready? he thought with quiet bitterness. Surely I would have fought death with all the power that was in me when I was a lusty youth, dreaming of what the years would bring—fortune and fame worthy of the house of Galilei. And now that I am old and crippled and blind, even now I would suffer a year longer, a month, or even a week that I might guide Vincenzio's clumsy fingers until he perfects my pendulum clock.

How my pulse falters and stumbles. If I only had my pulsifier, my little pendulum. . . . The pendulum! Yes, it all began that day in the cathedral when I watched the swinging pendulum and knew that I could refute Aristotle. And now I must end my labors, still working on a pendulum to measure time. But the circle is not complete; my work is still unfinished. So much more to record . . . those chapters on percussion. . . . Is it right, O Lord, for a man to labor for almost sixty years only to be called away against his will in the end, leaving his tools scattered and his work half finished on his table like an untidy apprentice eager for a holiday?

Yet I should be content—for I who have ever sought for

truth have found it in many places. Only once did I stray from the path. Lord, Thou hast suffered on the cross; Thy pain was heavy—but Thou couldst endure it because Thou wast God. But I was mortal man, and sick and afraid. I thought of Giordano Bruno at the stake and I repeated the words my judges put into my mouth.

Lord, Thou knowest my remorse and my shame. Since that hour when I sinned against the truth, I have never ceased to ask Thy forgiveness. Instead of the punishment I deserved, perhaps Thou didst strike me with blindness. I betrayed the vision Thou didst spread before me across the heavens, and Thou didst decree: Let his eyes delight no longer in the wonders that I have made!

Am I punished enough, O God? In the world to which Thou hast called me will my two good eyes be restored to me? Wilt Thou in Thy mercy permit me to continue my search among the stars? . . .

"He died peacefully," Vincenzio Galilei told Viviani, who arrived a few moments too late to bid his master farewell. "His hands no longer groped as they have since his blindness; he no longer wore that hurt, puzzled frown. Nay, he smiled, confident and unafraid. For a moment I believed that by some miracle he was able to see again."

EPILOGUE

"Truth's music, though the music-maker perish,
Liveth—for loving hearts of men to cherish:
The truth we dreamed as dying with our death
Some glory through the darkness quickeneth:
Truth liveth."

NEARLY A CENTURY passed. The worn body and restless brain of Galileo Galilei moldered into dust in an obscure corner of the Church of Santa Croce. For Rome had forbidden a more prominent place. A funeral oration was also forbidden, nor were Galileo's friends allowed to erect a public monument in his honor. The Church had decreed that it was not seemly to pay honor to a man condemned once as a heretic. Let those who loved Galileo be grateful that he was permitted to rest in consecrated ground.

Vincenzio Viviani succeeded his master as court mathematician. In his will the scientist set aside a large sum for a fitting monument for Galileo. With this legacy he left the request to be permitted to remain in death—as in life—beside his dear benefactor.

In the year 1737 one of the largest assemblies which Florence had ever seen gathered before the Church of Santa Croce, where so many of the mighty Tuscan dead lie buried. It seemed as though the entire city had come to pay honor to its long-neglected son. There were representatives of the church and state; scholars not only from every Italian university but also famous savants from all the European centers of learning. Florentine citizens in formal dress brushed shoulders with representatives of foreign governments; workers from the city, peddlers of flowers and ragged street boys waited impatiently.

There was a sudden reverent hush when the bodies of Galileo and Viviani were interred in their new resting place. Then came tributes of flowers, words of praise for the man whose glory had not dimmed but increased through the years.

Among those who watched the ceremonies were many who year after year had often stood in reverence beside the scientist's lonely grave. Now the monument and new tomb of Galileo stood in so prominent a spot that all who entered the church were challenged to do him honor.

Many more years were to pass before the teachings of Copernicus and Galileo were universally accepted. But in 1757 the much-disputed work of the humble canon was not included in the revised Index of prohibited books. By 1822 the Copernican system which Galileo had suffered to teach was freely taught in Catholic colleges. As every school child knows today the earth moves around the sun. And the minds of men move also in their search for greater knowledge.

"May Galileo Galilei rest in peace," murmured a white-haired scholar from Padua who, in his shabby cloak, walked as proudly as a king. "Today is the beginning. Someday he and the truth he sought will be vindicated before the world."

BIBLIOGRAPHY

Allan-Olney, Maey. *The Private Life of Galileo,* compiled from his correspondence and that of his daughter Sister Maria Celeste. Boston: Nichols & Noyes, 1870.

Armitage, Angus. *The World of Copernicus.* New York: (Henry Schuman, Inc., 1947, under title *Sun, Stand Thou Still*) Mentor Books, 1951.

Bevan, Rev. J. O. *University Life in the Olden Times.* London: Chapman and Hall, 1914.

Bolton, Sarah K. *Famous Men of Science.* New York: Thomas Y. Crowell, 1889.

Brewster, David S. *Martyrs of Science.* London: John Murray, 1841.

Campanella, Thomas. *The Defense of Galileo,* translated and edited by Grant McColley. Northampton, Mass.: Smith College Studies, 1912.

Cottler, Joseph, and Jaffe Haym. *Heroes of Civilization.* Boston: Little, Brown & Co., 1931.

Dampier, Sir William Cecil. *A History of Science.* New York: Macmillan, 1949.

De Harsanyi, Zsolt. *The Star Gazer,* translated from the Hungarian by Paul Tabor. New York: G. P. Putnam's Sons, 1939.

Durant, Will. *The Story of Philosophy.* New York: Simon & Schuster, 1926.

Ellis, William A. *Men Who Found Out.* London: Gerald Howe, 1929.

Fahie, John Joseph. *Galileo His Life and Work.* New York: James Pott & Co., 1903.

Foligno, Cesare. *The Story of Padua.* London: J. M. Dent & Sons, 1910.

Galilei, Galileo. *Dialogues Concerning Two New Sciences,* translated from the Italian and Latin by Henry Crew and Alfonso de Salvio. New York: Macmillan, 1914.

Hawks, Captain Ellison. *Astronomy.* London: T. C. & E. C. Jack, 1914.

Horst, Fertel. *Mediaeval and Modern University Ideas and Students' Life.* Montreal: Southampton Press, 1932.

Hull, Ernest R. *Galileo and His Condemnation.* London: Catholic Truth Society, 1923.

Lucas, E. V. *A Wanderer in Florence.* New York: Macmillan, 1927.

Macpherson, Hector. *Makers of Astronomy.* Oxford: Clarendon Press, 1933.

Moulton, Forest Ray. *Consider the Heavens.* New York: Doubleday, Doran & Co., 1935.

Namer, Emile. *Galileo, Searcher of the Heavens,* translated from the French by Sibyl Harris. New York: R. M. McBride, 1931.

Pendray, G. Edward. *Men, Mirrors and Stars.* New York: Harper & Brothers, 1935, or revised edition, 1946.

Schevill, Ferdinand. *History of Florence.* New York: Harcourt, Brace & Co., 1936.

Thomas, Henry, and Dana, Lee. *Living Biographies of Great Scientists.* Garden City: Doubleday, Doran, 1941.

Thwing, Charles F. *Universities of the World.* New York: Macmillan, 1911.

Vaughn, Herbert M. *Studies in the Italian Renaissance.* New York: E. P. Dutton & Co., 1929.

Willocks, M. P. *The Laughing Philosopher, a Life of Rabelais.* London: George Allen & Unwin, Ltd., 1950.

Woodbury, David O. *The Glass Giant of Palomar.* New York: Dodd, Mead & Co., 1940.

Zweig, Stefan. *Erasmus of Rotterdam.* New York: The Viking Press, 1934.

————. *John Milton,* Prefatory Memoir. London: Frederick Warne & Co.

Catholic Encyclopedia   Compton's Pictured Encyclopedia
Chamber's Encyclopedia   Encyclopedia Americana
Collier's Encyclopedia   Encyclopaedia Britannica
    The World Book Encyclopedia

Blumenstock, David I. "Weather Instruments." New York: *Scientific American*, December, 1951.

Buechel, William W. "Aquinas, Sainted Fool." Chicago: *Extension,* December, 1951.

Dibner, Vern. "Moving the Obelisk." New York: *Scientific American*, June, 1951.

INDEX